THE ALTE... GCSE GUIDES

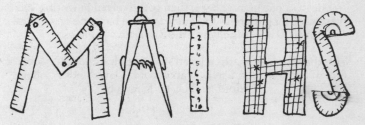

MATHS

EXAM SUCCESS WITHOUT THE STRESS

Kjartan Poskitt

Illustrated by Polly Dunbar

SCHOLASTIC

To Bridget without whom I'd be lost.

Armed with an engineering degree from Durham, Kjartan Poskitt
set out as a pub piano player, then got involved in writing and
presenting for children's t.v. Since then he has gone on to write
over 30 books including the *Murderous Maths* series.

With thanks to our maths educational consultants, Mike Moon of
Mount School, York, David Watkins of D'Oeverbrooks College,
Oxford, and Diana Kimpton.

Scholastic Children's Books,
Commonwealth House, 1-19 New Oxford Street,
London, WC1A 1NU, UK
A division of Scholastic Ltd
London - New York - Toronto - Sydney - Auckland
Mexico City - New Delhi - Hong Kong

First published in the UK by Scholastic Ltd, 2001

Typeset by M Rules
Printed by Cox & Wyman Ltd, Reading, Berks.

10 9 8 7 6 5 4 3 2 1

Contents

Why do maths?

Whatever you aim to do in life, you're going to need some maths. If you're a designer or engineer you need to know about measurements and shapes, if you're a sports star you'll need to understand averages and data, and if you're a fabulously rich pop musician then you'll need a bit of maths to help you enjoy those long winter evenings when you're counting your money. In fact whatever you do and wherever in the world you end up, maths is one subject you really need. That's why when you leave school, you are nearly always asked if you've got a GCSE in maths. It's about the most useful thing you can have apart from being able to write your name and get yourself dressed.

So what do you need to know?

There are three levels of exam you can take:

F: the **foundation level** gives you a chance to concentrate on the more basic stuff and they make the questions a bit easier. If you're more comfortable going for a lower grade, then this is for you.

I: the **intermediate level** brings in some tougher bits, and if you do well you can get a higher grade.

H: the **highest level** has everything they can chuck at you and if you can roll it up and chuck it back you'll get a top grade.

Each section in the book is marked **F**, **I** or **H** to act as a rough guide to what you should know. Obviously, *everybody* needs to know the F bits, intermediate people need the F and I bits and the H people need the lot.

Does this book cover everything?

Just about everything for the foundation level is in here, but intermediate and higher level people may find they have come across one or two topics that aren't included. The trouble is that to cover every possible item that might come up for everyone in the country at any level would double the length of the book. (And double the price!) However, if you can deal with everything sandwiched between this page and the back cover, you'll get 95% and your maths teacher will carry a photo of you in his or her wallet for ever.

There are also a few tips on how to make your life easier and how to impress the examiners. And in chapter five there is some helpful and hopefully calming advice for the dreaded day of your GCSE maths exam.

What will this book do for you?
You've already had a few maths lessons and maybe even seen some old exam papers, so hopefully you've already found some bits of maths that you could understand.

- This book is to help clear up the bits that you find confusing, and to do this it explains each subject right through from the simplest starting details to the finish.

- Most things are explained step by step *using words as well as numbers* to give you the best possible chance of understanding what's going on. (This is why the book is as big as it is.)

- You might find you can skip a lot of the simple stuff including the meanings of certain words and explanations of things like degrees and shapes. However, if you get stuck on a section then get right back to the basics and work it through.

- Even if you've heard it all before in the classroom, when you've got it all written out in front of you you can take your time over it.

Is reading this book all you need to do to pass?

Can you imagine lying on the sofa watching an exercise video and wondering why you're still an unfit slob? Is that sad or what? It's the same as staring at this book and thinking you'll breeze through the exams. There's no short cut, you've GOT to practise doing maths and this book includes a few examples to try. Even if they look obvious, do yourself a favour and work them through to check you know what's going on. You should also get hold of some suitable test papers for the correct level of exams you're taking and try these too. Apart from getting better at the subject, you'll soon find which bits of maths you can rely on to get a few guaranteed marks! This will build your confidence for tackling everything else.

How many marks are the exams worth?

Exams are set by different organizations called "boards" and it depends which board you're trying to impress. There's not too much difference between them, so generally you can expect two written papers which are each worth 40% of your total GCSE maths marks. The remaining 20% comes from your school coursework where you have to show how well you can understand, analyse and explain things.

Simple. The book is divided into four main sections: Numbers, Algebra, Shape and Data. Each section has several topics which are split up and listed here.

There are two ways of using this book:

- You could work right through the book taking each section from start to finish. You might like to keep track of your progress by ticking off the boxes of the sections you've covered.

- You can check up on individual topics you are unsure of. If the section you need still leaves you unsure, go back a few pages and read the sections that lead up to it.

☐ The tick boxes indicate what you need to know for the level you are taking. This is only a rough guide – if you have been told that you need to know a topic that doesn't have a tick box for your level, then you should still look at it!

* These sections contain information that is most likely to be tested.

Numbers

Data

Numbers just don't add up!

Numbers are what most of maths is made out of, so to start with we have to understand exactly what they are. This chapter takes you all the way from the basic 1-2-3 to weird stuff like irrational numbers, so even if the first few sections look mind-numbingly obvious, don't imagine that it's all going to be that easy!

F: Using digits to write numbers

Just a little point to clear up before we go on: there are ten different digits which are 1, 2, 3, 4, 5, 6, 7, 8, 9, 0. We use digits to write down numbers in the same way that we use letters to write words. The clever bit is that digits are worth different amounts depending on where they are "placed". Let's look at the number 6,780,291. Here's what the different places are worth:

6	7	8	0	2	9	1
millions	100,000s	10,000s	1,000s	100s	10s	units

This all might seem rather obvious, but it gets more important when we look at how decimals work later on. There are two sorts of question examiners might ask just to warm you up:

1. Write out: 435; 72,005 and 34,278,201 in words.

2. Put these numbers in order starting with the lowest:
a) 212 122 211 121
b) 4756 5674 4576 5467

Answers on page 304.

Arithmetic

There will be an "arithmetic" section of your exams where you are NOT allowed to use a calculator because the examiners want to see that you can add, subtract, multiply and divide.

TOP TIP

Show your workings! Although getting the right answer is important, you need to show that you know what you are doing. If you work out a long sum but make a tiny slip and get it wrong, you might still get some marks if you show that you know how it all works. It's certainly more impressive than if you get the right answer with a lucky guess! Suppose a question asks you how much you must spend to buy a hamster for £2.50 and a cage for £12.75. The answer is £15.25, but imagine you are so nervous that you make a mistake and think it is £15.35. If you just write that down you'll lose both the marks this question carries. But if you write £2.50 + £12.75 = £15.35, you'll get one mark for using the right method even though you got the answer wrong. So always show your workings in every question, otherwise you may throw marks away.

The main reason to avoid using a calculator for as long as possible is that a calculator for arithmetic is like waterwings for swimming. If you never learn to swim without waterwings, then no matter how much you practise, you'll still be rather helpless. The same goes for calculators because if you always use a calculator right from the start, then you'll never completely understand what's going on.

I don't get it!

So do yourself a favour – as you work through this section DON'T REACH FOR THE CALCULATOR unless it says so.

F: Adding, subtracting, multiplying, dividing
The most basic sums in maths look like this:

$$
\begin{array}{cccc}
349 & 4448 & 927 & 1360 \div 16 \\
27 & -2739 & \times 15 & = \\
+5681 & \rule{2cm}{0.4pt} & \rule{1.5cm}{0.4pt} & \\
\rule{2cm}{0.4pt} & = & = & \\
= & & &
\end{array}
$$

You have to be able to do all these, so check you can do them right now before you go any further. (Answers on page 304.) Every exam will include a few sums like this, although they are often dressed up in problems such as:

A battleship has 4,779 rivets holding it together. How many rivets are needed for 27 battleships?

A genetically modified orchard produces 1,102 blue apples. If all its 29 trees are identical, how many apples does each tree produce?

Were you just about to skip these questions? Well don't, because you might not be as smart as you think. (Try them both, then look at the answers on page 304.)

This book assumes that you'll know how to work these sums out so we aren't going to deal with them here. If you aren't sure, then there are a few books which will remind you exactly what to do, the funniest of which is called *Murderous Maths: The Essential Arithmetricks*. In the meantime we'll just check on a couple of vital points. These might seem obvious, but don't underestimate them!

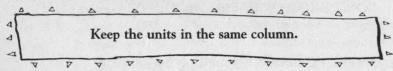

Keep the units in the same column.

If you're adding 245 + 37 + 1903, write it down with all of the units underneath each other like this:

$$\begin{array}{r} 245 \\ 37 \\ + \ 1903 \\ \hline \\ = \end{array}$$

This makes sure that the 10s, 100s and 1000s are all in the same columns too. If you're working with decimals, the decimal points must always be in a column and that keeps everything else in place.

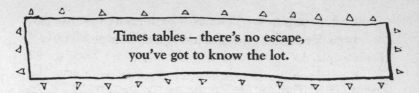

**Times tables – there's no escape,
you've got to know the lot.**

All sorts of smug people pretend to get by in maths without learning the tables properly but they always come to a ghastly end. Serves them right too.

You need to know the answer to sums like 7 × 3 and 5 × 9 so well that you don't have to stop to think. Make sure you know every answer from 1 × 1 to 10 × 10 (which isn't as bad as it sounds as pairs like 5 × 4 and 4 × 5 give the same answer). If there is one you always get wrong, then it's time for desperate action: make an extra-special effort to learn it or you might make a slip in the middle of a long exam question and lose lots of marks.

Suppose you keep getting 3 × 7 = 21 wrong. Try and make it fit your favourite tune – for instance you might find you just can't stop humming along and tapping your feet to "London bridge is falling down". Change the words to "three times seven is twenty-one". You can sing it in the shower. Or, even better, get out into the street and sing it out loud, especially if somebody you really fancy is just passing by. You will NEVER forget it for as long as you live.

Just out of interest, the "9 times" table is rather more fun than the others because the two digits in the answer *always* add up to 9. (For example, $9 \times 7 = 63$, and if you add up the $6 + 3$ you get 9.)

TOP TIP
For big sums, estimate what the answer should be first. It helps you spot mistakes. There's a section about estimations later on. They only take a few seconds and are always worth doing!

F: Understanding decimals

As you probably know, multiplying by 10 or 100 is easy: you move all the digits one or two places to the left (or, if you prefer to think of it the other way, you move the decimal point one or two places to the right). So $127 \times 10 = 1270$ and $344 \times 100 = 34,400$ and $5{\cdot}77 \times 10 = 57{\cdot}7$. Dividing is just as easy: you just move the digits to the right (or the decimal place to the left). So $540 \div 10 = 54$ and $354{\cdot}3 \div 100 = 3{\cdot}543$ and $7 \div 10 = 0{\cdot}7$ and $7 \div 100 = 0{\cdot}07$.

As the decimal point is so tiny, people usually put a zero in front of it to make it more obvious that it's there. You could write the answer to the last sum as $\cdot07$, but it's better to avoid confusion and write $0{\cdot}07$.

TOP TIP
Don't forget to put a "0" before a decimal point in exams – or your answers might look wrong!

If you had to work out 4 ÷ 1000 then you need to move the digit "4" three places to the right. If you move it one place you'd get 0·4, if you moved it a second place you'd get 0·04 and by the time you've moved it a third place you get 0·004. That's the correct answer you wanted: 4 ÷ 1000 = 0·004.

Let's just check we know the value of the places on the right hand side of the decimal point. For instance, here's what 5·9413 is worth:

5	·	9	4	1	3
units	decimal point	tenths	hundredths	thousandths	ten thousandths

Sometimes zeros are really important and sometimes they are not. If you play a video game and it shows your score as 000005700 then the first five zeros don't tell you anything. The game might just as well have given your score as 5700. Of course the last two zeros are vital because without them your score would only be 57 and you'd have to hide your head in shame. (By the way, if the game shows your score as 570000000 then you're playing way too much. Stop wasting your life and get out more.)

Honest, it's helping with my Maths GCSE.

When a decimal point is involved, it's the zeros at the end that don't tell you anything. If you have 0·007081000 then that's the same as 0·007081. You can live without the zeros at the end, but you need to keep the others.

F: Money

When we write pounds and pence, this is a form of decimals and we always use two decimal places. If you have £7 ÷ 10 you could say it makes £0·7. However there are 100 pence in £1 so instead of starting with £7, it helps to write £7·00. When we divide this by 10 we get £0·70 which is the same as 70p.

F: Multiplying and dividing with decimals

You know $3 \times 7 = 21$ and therefore $21 \div 3 = 7$ and $21 \div 7 = 3$. Let's see how we can use these facts to solve other sums quickly:

3 × 0·7   As 0·7 = 7 ÷ 10 you can write $3 \times 0·7$ as $3 \times 7 \div 10$. So you can work out the whole sum like this: $3 \times 0·7 = 3 \times 7 \div 10 = 21 \div 10 = 2·1$

0·003 × 70 $0·003 = 3 \div 1000$ and $70 = 7 \times 10$. The sum becomes: $0·003 \times 70 = 3 \div 1000 \times 7 \times 10 = 3 \times 7 \times 10 \div 1000 = 21 \div 100 = 0·21$. Remember to be extra careful when you're dividing! You are more likely to make mistakes if you don't think carefully.

21 ÷ 70   We know $21 \div 7 = 3$ but for this sum we are dividing by 70, so the answer will be 10 times smaller. Therefore $21 \div 70 = 0·3$. To write that down with numbers, remember: $70 = 7 \times 10$, so the sum becomes $21 \div (7 \times 10)$. Notice that we have to divide 21 by everything inside the bracket, so when we remove the bracket the sum becomes 21 ÷ 7 ÷ 10. Here's how the whole sum should look: 21 ÷ 70 = 21 ÷ (7 × 10) = 21 ÷ 7 ÷ 10 = 3 ÷ 10 = 0·3

21 ÷ 0·03 Here the 0·03 is 100 times smaller than 3. As we are dividing by a number 100 times smaller, the answer should be 100 times bigger. Let's see it: 21 ÷ 0·03 = 21 ÷ (3 ÷ 100) = 21 ÷ 3 × 100 = 7 × 100 = 700

In exams they may well give you a result such as: **427 × 119 = 50813**. They might then ask you to work out:

50813 ÷ 119 Simple! It's just 427.

50·813 ÷ 427 As 50813 ÷ 427 = 119 then you know the answer is going to have the digits 119. The question is, where's the decimal point? As 50·813 = 50813 ÷ 1000, the whole sum becomes: 50·813 ÷ 427 = 50813 ÷ 427 ÷ 1000 = 119 ÷ 1000 = 0·119

Go on and try these, and remember *no calculator*!

a) 4270 × 1·19 **b)** 508130 ÷ 42·7 **c)** 0·050813 ÷ 1190

Answers on page 304.

What numbers are

Every single number is different, and has different characteristics. For instance, the number 13 is very different from the number 12 even though it is only worth 1 more. Here we're going to have a look at why numbers are different and what help we can get from these differences.

F: Odd and even numbers

Even numbers divide by 2 and odd numbers don't. If you start with any even number and add or subtract 1, you always get an odd number. And if you start with any odd number and add or subtract 1 you always get an even number.

Wouldn't it be great if this was all you needed to know to pass the GCSE? Never mind. . .

F: Squares, cubes and how index numbers work

Often in maths numbers get multiplied by themselves. This is marked with a little number called an **index** (plural: **indices**). Look at these:

$3^2 = 3 \times 3 = 9$ This is "3 to the power of 2" or "3 squared".

$7^3 = 7 \times 7 \times 7 = 343$ This is "7 to the power of 3" or "7 cubed".

$5^4 = 5 \times 5 \times 5 \times 5 = 625$ This is "5 to the power of 4" but it doesn't have a fancy name.

$4^{-1} = \frac{1}{4}$ If the index is negative, then it's the **reciprocal** or "one over" the number.

$9^{-2} = \frac{1}{9^2} = \frac{1}{9 \times 9} = \frac{1}{81}$ Here the index of –2 indicates it's the reciprocal of the number squared.

$2^{-3} = \frac{1}{2^3} = \frac{1}{2 \times 2 \times 2} = \frac{1}{8}$ Another example of a negative index.

TOP TIP

Always write index numbers clearly! $5^4 = 625$ but if you write it carelessly it looks like 54. And NEVER make the mistake of thinking that 5^4 is the same as 5×4.

Roots

$7^2 = 49$ tell us that "seven squared equals 49". This can work the other way round. You might ask "What number squared is 49?" but it's more usual to say, "What is the *square root* of 49?" If you want the square root of a number, then the index number is $\frac{1}{2}$. Therefore $49^{\frac{1}{2}} = 7$. You can also write square roots as $\sqrt{49} = 7$.

This works for any index number, for example:

$2^5 = 32$ and so $32^{\frac{1}{5}} = 2$
$4^3 = 64$ and so $64^{\frac{1}{3}} = 4$

$64^{\frac{1}{3}}$ is sometimes called the **cube root** of 64 and written $\sqrt[3]{64}$.

Multiplying and dividing powers

When you multiply numbers with powers, you add the indices:
$3^6 \times 3^2 = 3^{6+2} = 3^8$

When you divide numbers with powers you subtract the indices:
$6^4 \div 6^3 = 6^{4-3} = 6^1 = 6$ (Notice that $6^1 = 6$.)

And anything to the power of "0" equals 1:
$7^3 \times 7^4 \div 7^7 = 7^{(3+4-7)} = 7^0 = 1$

Here are some quick questions that can come up. Try them yourself before checking the answers:

Evaluate: a) 5^2 b) 2^{-5} c) $3^{-3} \div 3^2$ d) $4^{-\frac{1}{2}}$ e) $\left(\frac{9}{25}\right)^{-\frac{1}{2}}$ f) $(64 \times 27)^{\frac{1}{3}}$

Answers on page 305.

F: Triangle numbers

Triangle numbers are dead cute and if you really get into maths then you'll find that they turn up in all sorts of odd places. However we've got exams to pass, so just for now all you need to know is what they are. It's easiest to understand by laying out counters to make bigger and bigger triangle shapes.

Here's how the first four triangles would look:

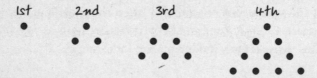

You can easily tell which triangle is which by counting the number of rows. (Obviously with the 1st triangle number there is only one very short row!)

If you look at the triangles and add up the counters in each row, you can work out the first four triangle numbers:

1st triangle number = 1
2nd triangle number = 1 + 2 = 3
3rd triangle number = 1 + 2 + 3 = 6
4th triangle number = 1 + 2 + 3 + 4 = 10

You'll notice that the 2nd triangle number is the same as the 1st triangle number + 2. The 3rd triangle number is the 2nd triangle number + 3 and so on. Before reading on: What do you think the 5th triangle number is? (Answer on page 305.)

If you need to work out a triangle number, it isn't always convenient to be setting out loads of counters but there is another way.

Suppose we wanted the 10th triangle number. We would have to add 10 + 9 + 8 + 7 + 6 + 5 + 4 + 3 + 2 + 1 and get 55. This is the right answer, but we're working too hard. What you do is multiply the 10 by the next number up, which is 11. You then divide the answer by 2. You get $10 \times 11 \div 2 = 55$.

This works for any number, so for the 5th triangle number you multiply 5×6 then divide by 2. You get $5 \times 6 \div 2 = 15$ which is what we expected.

For **H** level only: you can describe this process much more neatly by saying the algebraic formula for the "n"th triangle number T_n is: $T_n = \frac{1}{2}n(n + 1)$.

What are the 7th, 20th and 99th triangle numbers?

Answers on page 305.

F: Factors and primes

A factor is any number that divides exactly into another number. For instance 1, 2 and 4 are all the factors of 4. 1, 2, 4, 8 and 16 are all the factors of 16. 1, 2, 3, 4, 6, 9, 12, 18 and 36 are all the factors of 36.

If you are asked to write all the factors of a number out in a row, you can do a rough check. Look at the factors for 36 and multiply the first and last. You get $1 \times 36 = 36$. Then try the next two factors, working towards the centre of the row. You get $2 \times 18 = 36$. Multiply the next two and you'll get $3 \times 12 = 36$ and so on. Finally, if you get one number left in the middle, square it. In this case you get $6^2 = 36$. If one of the sums doesn't work out, you've got a missing factor.

What are all the factors of 32, 50, and 72?

Answers on page 305.

You might be forgiven for thinking that the bigger the number is then the more factors it will have, but no! For example the factors of 1009 are just 1 and 1009. Numbers like this are called prime numbers.

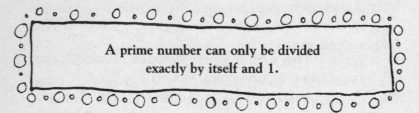

A prime number can only be divided exactly by itself and 1.

There is no limit to how big prime numbers can be – for instance 207,622,273 is a prime number, but it's only a baby compared to some that have been discovered. However, we're only going to look at the smallest primes: 2 3 5 7 11 13 17 19 23 29 31 37 . . .

You'll see 2 is prime because it can only divide by itself and 1. As it happens 2 is a bit special as it is the only even prime number. Of course any other even number will divide by 2.

What about 1? Well it can only divide exactly by itself and 1, but it is *itself* 1, so is it prime? Mathematicians with nothing better to do have massive arguments about this...

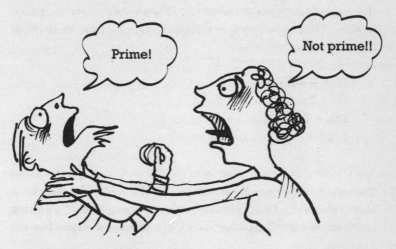

But as we've got exams to pass we'll leave them to it. Just for now, though, we'll say that 1 *isn't* prime.

Write out the odd numbers between 30 and 60 and underline the prime numbers.

Answers on page 305.

F: Composite numbers
Prime numbers are often nicknamed "building blocks" because:

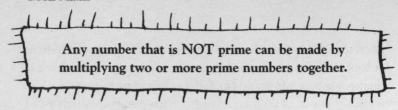

Any number that is NOT prime can be made by multiplying two or more prime numbers together.

Numbers that are not prime are called "composite" numbers because they are *composed* of prime numbers. The clever bit is that every composite number has its own special set of "prime factors". Here is how a few composite numbers are made from their prime factors:

$$12 = 2 \times 2 \times 3$$
$$48 = 2 \times 2 \times 2 \times 2 \times 3$$
$$221 = 13 \times 17$$
$$3003 = 3 \times 7 \times 11 \times 13$$

You'll notice that quite often you use the same prime factor more than once, and if you get a number like 81 you'll find the prime factors are $3 \times 3 \times 3 \times 3$. (This is the same as saying $81 = 3^4$.) Writing a number like this is called writing it as a **product of prime factors**.

What's the use of prime factors?

If you're juggling about with several big numbers at once, stripping them down into their prime factors means that you can often spot short cuts. It's a bit like having to give a speech in front of lots of stuffy people: suppose you could strip them down to their pants first – it would make your life so much easier.

That's better!

F: How to break a number into prime factors

You start with your number then try dividing the prime numbers into it starting with 2 then 3 then 5 and so on until you just have "1" left at the end. It's easiest to understand if we just see it happen, so let's pick a number to play with. How about 60?

What we're doing	Prime factors	What's left
We're starting with 60		60
Does 60 divide by 2? Yes it does and we get 60 ÷ 2 = 30. This means we have our first prime factor of 2 and we have 30 left over.	2	30
We now try dividing 2 into 30. Yes! 30 ÷ 2 = 15	2	15

We now try dividing 2 into 15, but
it won't go. Let's try the next prime
number which is 3. 15 ÷ 3 = 5   3   5

We've just got 5 left, and 3 won't go
into it. Never mind, we move on to
try our next prime number and
guess what? It's 5. 5 ÷ 5 =1   5   1

We've just got 1 left and so we've finished.

When we look back up the column of prime factors we see that
we've got 2, 2, 3 and 5. These are the prime factors of 60 – and if
you want to check you can just multiply them up again. You'll find
$2 \times 2 \times 3 \times 5 = 60$. You could also write this as $2^2 \times 3 \times 5 = 60$.

Let's try breaking down another number. How about 1911?

What we're doing	Prime factors	What's left
We're starting with 1911		1911
1911 ÷ 2 *won't go*.		
Move on to 3. 1911 ÷ 3 = 637	3	637
Try 3 again but 637 ÷ 3 won't go.		
Try 5 but 637 ÷ 5 won't go.		
Try 7: 637 ÷ 7 = 91	7	91
Try 7 again: 91 ÷ 7 = 13	7	13

Hey! We realize that 13 is a prime
number so let's skip to 13 ÷ 13 = 1   13   1

Finished! The prime factors of 1911 turn out to be 3, 7, 7, 13.

Here are the sorts of questions you might get:

**1. Write these numbers as products of their prime
factors: a) 1078 b) 1029 c) 665**

**2. You can write 72 as $2^x \times 3^y$. What are the values of
x and y?**

Answers on page 305.

F: When will numbers divide?
There are several handy short cuts if you want to find out if a
number will divide by 2 or 3 or 5.

2: Very easy – any even number will always divide by 2. Odd
   numbers will not.
3: This is a neat trick. Add up the digits in the number. If the total
   divides by 3 then so will the number! For instance, will 279
   divide by 3? Add up 2+7+9 = 18. Since we know 18 divides by
   3, then so will 279. Will 514 divide by 3? Add up 5+1+4 = 10.
   This does NOT divide by 3 so we know 514 won't either.
5: Very easy – any number ending in 5 or 0 will divide by 5.

These little tricks help with the first steps of breaking numbers
into prime factors.

Fractions

F: When you divide one number by another, if it doesn't go exactly you get a fraction such as $\frac{3}{8}$ or $\frac{5}{6}$. The number on the top is called the **numerator** and the number on the bottom is called the **denominator**, but as that all sounds a bit heavy we'll just keep calling them the top and the bottom.

Fractions are certain to turn up during the exams and you won't be allowed to use your calculator, so give this section special attention. First let's look at the different types of fractions...

Vulgar fraction	This is a fraction such as $\frac{3}{8}$ where the top is smaller than the bottom. If the top is nearly as big as the bottom such as $\frac{9}{10}$ then the fraction is nearly equal to 1.
Improper fraction	This is a fraction like $\frac{11}{6}$ where the top is bigger than the bottom. Unless you are about to do a calculation with it, you should convert it into a . . .
Mixed fraction	This is when you have a number *and* a fraction such as $1\frac{5}{6}$. This is how you should present answers. However, if you are about to do a sum with it, you would usually convert it into an improper fraction.

We'll see how to do the conversions in a minute.

F: Making fractions look nicer

If $3 \div 6$ came up in an exam, you *could* give the answer as $\frac{3}{6}$ which is "three sixths" but you probably wouldn't get full marks for it. The reason is that $\frac{3}{6}$ will "reduce" or "cancel down" and you should ALWAYS do it. Here's the trick involved:

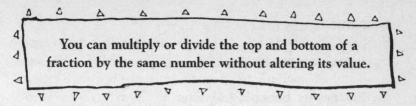

You can multiply or divide the top and bottom of a fraction by the same number without altering its value.

So to reduce a fraction you should divide top and bottom by the highest number you can. (This number is called the Highest Common Factor or HCF.) In the case of $\frac{3}{6}$ you can divide both the top and bottom by 3 and you get $\frac{1}{2}$.

Even when fractions are bigger you can use the same process. Suppose you end up with $\frac{24}{36}$, you could divide top and bottom by 12 to get: $\frac{24 \div 12}{36 \div 12} = \frac{2}{3}$.

If you're not sure what the HCF is then divide through by smaller numbers in turn. In this case you might start by dividing top and bottom by 4 to get: $\frac{24 \div 4}{36 \div 4} = \frac{6}{9}$ and then divide through by 3 to get: $\frac{6 \div 3}{9 \div 3} = \frac{2}{3}$.

TOP TIP

Always cancel down fractions where possible and don't give improper fractions in your answers. If you end up with an improper fraction, then you should convert it to a mixed fraction. Suppose you've spent two hours cracking a brilliantly fiendish sum and get an answer of $\frac{26}{4}$. It isn't immediately clear how big $\frac{26}{4}$ is (e.g. is it bigger than 10? Less than 3?). What you do is divide the bottom into the top, so 4 into 26 goes 6 times with a remainder of 2. This gives you a mixed answer of $6\frac{2}{4}$. Don't write this down though – because the $\frac{2}{4}$ will cancel down to $\frac{1}{2}$. Your final answer should be $6\frac{1}{2}$.

As you can see, an answer of $6\frac{1}{2}$ is a lot more help than $\frac{26}{4}$ because it's much easier to appreciate how big $6\frac{1}{2}$ really is.

Now it's time for some practice:

1. Reduce: $\frac{27}{36}$ $\frac{24}{52}$ $\frac{33}{121}$

2. Convert to mixed fractions: $\frac{11}{4}$ $\frac{43}{10}$ $\frac{31}{7}$

3. Convert to improper fractions: $2\frac{3}{5}$ $1\frac{14}{17}$ $10\frac{6}{7}$

Answers on page 305.

F: Multiplying and dividing fractions

- To **multiply two fractions,** just times the tops together and times the bottoms together: $\frac{2}{3} \times \frac{7}{8} = \frac{2\times7}{3\times8} = \frac{14}{24}$

  But don't forget to cancel down. If you divide this one through by 2 you get a final answer of $\frac{7}{12}$.

- To **divide one fraction by another,** turn the "dividing" fraction upside down and multiply! $\frac{5}{6} \div \frac{2}{3} = \frac{5}{6} \times \frac{3}{2}$ You then go on to work out: $\frac{5}{6} \times \frac{3}{2} = \frac{15}{12} = 1\frac{3}{12} = 1\frac{1}{4}$

  You'll see that we converted the $\frac{15}{12}$ into a mixed fraction, then reduced the $\frac{3}{12}$ to $\frac{1}{4}$. This is because we are stylish and groovy people.

- To **divide a whole number by a fraction,** again just turn the dividing fraction upside down and multiply. It can help to write your whole number with a "1" underneath like this: $4 \div \frac{2}{5} = \frac{4}{1} \times \frac{5}{2} = \frac{20}{2} = 10$

- To **divide a fraction by a whole number,** again it can help to pretend your whole number has a "1" underneath. Look at this: $\frac{7}{8} \div 3 = \frac{7}{8} \div \frac{3}{1} = \frac{7}{8} \times \frac{1}{3} = \frac{7}{24}$

Calculate these sums and reduce your answers as much as possible:

a) $\frac{4}{5} \times \frac{5}{8}$ **b)** $2\frac{2}{3} \times 1\frac{1}{4}$ **c)** $6 \div 1\frac{5}{7}$ **d)** $3\frac{1}{4} \div 2\frac{3}{5}$

Answers on page 305.

F: Adding and subtracting fractions

You can only add or subtract fractions if they have the same denominator – i.e. the same number on the bottom. There's a bit of common sense involved here. Think about this sum: $\frac{3}{5} + \frac{1}{5}$.

We need to add three fifths to one fifth. Suppose you were adding three sheep to one sheep, how many sheep would you end up with? Four of course! It's the same with fifths, so three fifths plus one fifth makes four fifths. Let's see it with numbers: $\frac{3}{5} + \frac{1}{5} = \frac{3+1}{5} = \frac{4}{5}$.

If the numbers on the bottom are not the same, then you have to convert them. Suppose you have to add one quarter to five eighths. That's a bit like adding one cow to five pigs – you can't do it. What you have to do is convert them both into something that you can add together. Converting cows and pigs is a tough job, you'll be all night in the laboratory slicing them up and making a really gross mess, but luckily quarters and eighths are much simpler.

Let's see what the sum looks like with numbers: $\frac{1}{4} + \frac{5}{8}$.

Remember that you can multiply the top and bottom of any fraction with the same number, and it will still have the same value. In this case, let's multiply the top and bottom of the $\frac{1}{4}$ by 2. We get $\frac{2}{8}$ which is a lot more useful. Let's look at our sum again: $\frac{1 \times 2}{4 \times 2} + \frac{5}{8} = \frac{2}{8} + \frac{5}{8} = \frac{2+5}{8} = \frac{7}{8}$.

Sometimes you have to convert BOTH fractions. How about this sum, for instance: $\frac{3}{4} - \frac{2}{3}$.

One fraction has a 4 on the bottom and the other has a 3. The way to do this is to multiply each fraction through by the other's bottom! This might seem a bit odd, but look what happens. You get: $\frac{3 \times 3}{4 \times 3} = \frac{9}{12}$ and $\frac{2 \times 4}{3 \times 4} = \frac{8}{12}$.

We can now work out this sum in "twelfths" (and don't forget that this sum is a subtraction!): $\frac{9}{12} - \frac{8}{12} = \frac{9-8}{12} = \frac{1}{12}$.

How about $\frac{5}{6} - \frac{3}{8}$? (This is a tougher question than you'll get at foundation level.) You could just go ahead and multiply each fraction by the other's bottom and get: $\frac{5 \times 8}{6 \times 8} - \frac{3 \times 6}{8 \times 6} = \frac{40-18}{48} = \frac{22}{48} = \frac{11}{24}$.

There is nothing wrong with this but it's a good idea to try to use the lowest number you can on the bottom. In this case we're looking for the lowest number that will divide by both 6 and 8 which turns out to be 24. To convert the $\frac{5}{6}$ you ask yourself: how many times does 6 go into 24? Answer: 4 times – so multiply the top by 4. You get: $\frac{5 \times 4}{24} = \frac{20}{24}$.

You then convert the $\frac{3}{8}$ by asking: how many times does 8 go into 24? Answer: 3 times, so it's: $\frac{3 \times 3}{24} = \frac{9}{24}$.

Now you just finish the sum: $\frac{20-9}{24} = \frac{11}{24}$.

Make sure you've understood all this by trying these yourself then checking the answers on page 305:

a) $\frac{1}{2} - \frac{1}{6}$ **b)** $\frac{3}{8} + \frac{3}{4} - \frac{1}{2}$ **c)** $\frac{7}{16} + \frac{1}{2} - \frac{3}{8}$

d) $\frac{4}{5} - \frac{1}{4}$ **e)** $\frac{3}{4} + \frac{7}{10}$

Percentages

F: Percentages are just one particular form of fraction. They are "hundredths" ("cent" comes from the Latin word *centum* which means "a hundred", and in maths "per" means "divided by"). If you have 1%, then this is the same as one hundredth or $\frac{1}{100}$.

You may well get some quick questions such as:

What is 30% of 20?

TOP TIP
"Of" in maths means "multiplied by".

All this is asking is: "What is 30% × 20?" All you do is convert the 30% into a fraction and get: $\frac{30}{100} \times 20 = \frac{600}{100} = 6$.

Quite often percentage sums involve money, so let's see how one works:

What is 15% of £12?

This becomes: $\frac{15}{100} \times £12 = £\frac{180}{100} = £1\cdot8$.

Of course you don't leave the answer as £1·8 because with money you always work to two decimal places to show the pence. The answer should be £1·80.

What is a) 5% of 40   b) 12% of £70   c) 95% of 700 d) 25% of £17?

Answers on page 306.

41

F: Decimals as percentages

The reason people use percentages is that they are easy to add up and subtract – as you've seen when you start mixing up fractions, it can all get a bit messy. The trick is to know how to convert fractions and decimals into percentages – all you do is multiply by 100 and slap % on the end! Let's see how it works.

Suppose a national survey discovers that 0·07 of the entire population owns one single green sock. By the time this sort of fascinating information gets on the news, they'll have converted it into a percentage. Let's recall what decimal places are worth:

0 . 0 7

units decimal point tenths hundredths

You'll see that 0·07 is the same as 7 hundredths – which is 7%. Alternatively, we can work out 0·07 × 100 = 7%. What this is saying is that out of every one hundred people, seven of them own one single green sock. By the way, 100% is the same as $\frac{100}{100}$ and therefore 100% = 1.

Let's see how you're getting on:

Convert these decimals into percentages: a) 0·39 b) 21·6 c) 0·02674

Answers on page 306.

F: Fractions as percentages

Suppose you have $\frac{2}{5}$ and you want to make it into a percentage. Again, you just multiply it by 100 and put % on the end. The sum would look like this: $\frac{2}{5} \times 100 = \frac{2 \times 100}{5} = \frac{200}{5} = 200 \div 5 = 40\%$. You've done it!

Sometimes questions are worded like this:

1. What is 14 as a percentage of 56?

2. What is 85 as a percentage of 50?

All they're asking is for you to convert $\frac{14}{56}$ and $\frac{85}{50}$ into percentages. What do you get? (Answers on page 306.)

It helps to remember that halves, quarters, fifths and tenths convert to exact percentages like this: $\frac{1}{2}$ = 50%, $\frac{1}{4}$ = 25%, $\frac{3}{4}$ = 75%, $\frac{1}{5}$ = 20%, $\frac{1}{10}$ = 10%.

Some fractions such as eighths and sixteenths will also convert exactly, although you need to put in some decimals like this: $\frac{1}{8}$ = 12·5%, $\frac{3}{8}$ = 37·5%, $\frac{1}{16}$ = 6·25%, $\frac{15}{16}$ = 93·75%.

There are a lot of fractions that you can't write down as *exact* percentages – here are a few you should be aware of: $\frac{1}{3}$ = 33·3%, $\frac{2}{3}$ = 66·7%, $\frac{1}{6}$ = 16·7%, $\frac{5}{6}$ = 83·3%.

If you have to add, subtract or compare different fractions, converting them into percentages can sometimes help.

Arrange these into order of size starting with the smallest:
a) 61% $\frac{3}{8}$ 0·72 13·12% $\frac{4}{5}$ 2·5 $\frac{7}{8}$
b) $\frac{3}{10}$ $\frac{1}{3}$ 33% $\frac{30}{99}$

Answers on page 306.

I: Percentage increase and decrease
When percentages go up or down, be slightly careful. The trick is...

> **TOP TIP**
> Always treat the original number before the increase or decrease as 100%.

This will make sense when we see a couple of examples:

> **A sports stadium holds 35,000 people. Next year it plans to increase capacity by 15%. How many people will it hold then?**

The original number is 35,000, so treat this as 100%. When the stadium has been altered, the new capacity will be 100% + 15% = 115%. To get the answer you just multiply this percentage by the original capacity. You can write 115% as $\frac{115}{100}$ or even 1·15 so the sum is: 35,000 × $\frac{115}{100}$ = 40,250 people.

Another way to deal with this sum is to just work out how many more people the stadium will hold. This is 15% of 35,000 which is the same as $\frac{15}{100}$ × 35,000 = 5,250. It already holds 35,000 people so next year it will hold 35,000 + 5,250 = 40,250 people.

> **A CD player is reduced by 20% in a sale. If the sale price is £60, what was the original cost?**

A lot of people get confused here! Remember to treat the *original* cost as 100%. Therefore when this was reduced by 20%, it meant that the sale cost is 100% − 20% = 80%. This means that £60 is 80% of the original price. Suppose you were doing the sum the other way round starting with the original price and reducing it to 80%, you would work out: original cost × 80% = sale cost. Therefore original cost = sale cost ÷ 80% = sale cost ÷ $\frac{80}{100}$ = sale cost × $\frac{100}{80}$ = £60 × 100 ÷ 80 = £75. Or if you prefer you can work it out like this: 80% = £60; 1% = £$\frac{60}{80}$; 100% = £$\frac{60}{80}$ × 100 = £75.

Out of a total factory workforce of 420 people, 63 were off sick. What percentage were working?

First find how many people were working: 420 − 63 = 357. The fraction of workers is $\frac{357}{420}$ so the percentage is $\frac{357}{420}$ × 100 = 85%.

30% of cars parked in a street are red. If there are 56 cars of other colours, how many cars in total are there? If 45% of all the cars drive off, how many are left?

Your turn. (Answers on page 306.)

Rounding off

F: Suppose you counted all the hairs on your head and got 104,573. This long jumble of digits is a bit messy, and what's more people might think you're a bit sad if you knew this number *exactly*. To make it tidier, you could make the last two digits into zeros and so tell the world that you have 104,500 hairs. What you've done here is **rounded down** to the nearest hundred. Otherwise you could have said you've got 104,600 hairs in which case you've **rounded up** to the nearest hundred. So which is better?

If you think about 104,573, you can see it comes in between 104,500 and 104,600. The trick of **rounding off** is to pick which of these values is closer. There's a simple rule:

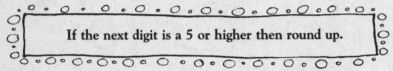

If the next digit is a 5 or higher then round up.

In this case, the next digit is a "7" so to round off properly you should say you've got 104,600 hairs on your head. If you wanted to round off to the nearest 1000 you'd say you had 105,000 hairs on your head. What if you wanted to round off to the nearest 10,000? You'd have 100,000 hairs. (Note: if you rounded 105,000 to the nearest 10,000 you'd get 110,000. However, you must remember that the number you are rounding is 104,573. Don't round off a number then round it off some more if you can help it!)

F: Significant figures

If you need to round off to hundreds, you make the number into a whole one ending with 00. To round off to thousands you make a whole number ending with 000. However, sometimes you are told how many *significant figures* (or *significant digits*) you need to work to. To round off 560,852,372 to FOUR significant figures, you use the rounding rule to write the first four figures or digits and turn all the others into zeros. So, as the fifth figure is a "5", your answer is 560,900,000.

Rounding off decimals works in a similar way. If you put 3 ÷ 140

46

into a calculator, you get 0·02142857. If you are told to give this answer to 5 significant figures, *first you write down the zeros at the front* then write down the next 5 digits. Of course, when you come to the fifth digit, check to see if you need to round up or round down. In this case you'd need to round up so you'd finish with 0·021429.

Just to make this clear, here are some random numbers rounded to different amounts:

number	2 sig. figs.	3 sig. figs.	4 sig. figs.
1,246,991	1,200,000	1,250,000	1,247,000
103	100	103	103·0
997	1000	997	997·0
12·098	12	12·1	12·10

It might seem odd that when 997 was rounded to 2 figures it became 1000. That's because 997 is nearer to 1000 than to 990. You'll also notice that when numbers were rounded to 4 significant figures, there's sometimes a zero at the end after the decimal point. This is just a slick way of saying the number is accurate to four figures rather than three and is one case where you shouldn't leave out the zero at the end of a decimal number.

F: Decimal places

Quite often you'll be asked to give an answer to "two decimal places" or "three decimal places". This might be written as 2 d.p. or 3 d.p. This is just telling you how many figures to give *after* the decimal point.

Suppose you had to work out 322 ÷ 15 to 3 d.p. First you should work it out to *four* decimal places – you'd get 21·4666 – then round it off to three, so you'd end up with 21·467. If you'd just worked it out to three places and then stopped you'd have given the answer as 21·466 which isn't nearly as cool as saying 21·467. In later life this attention to detail could mean the difference between cleaning up on the stock market and cleaning out the stock market.

F: An "appropriate degree of accuracy"

This is often sneaked into another question. They give you a sum and then ask for an answer with an "appropriate degree of accuracy". They don't tell you how many significant figures they want, or how many decimal places, they just want you to think it out for yourself. In other words the examiner is sitting there with a smug little grin saying "I know exactly what I want but I'm not going to tell you, so you have to guess." It's like when you're going out with somebody and it's their birthday and they know *exactly* what they want you to give them – but they won't tell you. Although they expect you to guess, they can be quite stroppy if you're wrong. To be honest, the best thing to do is to dump them and if they start bleating for a reason why, tell them a maths book told you to do it.

Let's say you're working out $645 \div 19$. If you worked it out for ages you might get 33·947368 which is *eight* significant figures. Yes it's impressive – especially if you did it without a calculator – but it will make you seem slightly mad. On the other hand if you just gave the answer as 30, then that's *one* significant figure and you'll look lazy.

TOP TIP

In exams, give answers to one more significant figure than the question. Look at the longest number involved – here it's 645 which is three digits. Therefore if you give the answer to four digits (and round it off correctly) you'll get 33·95 which looks pretty cool all round.

Estimations

F: Whenever you're doing a sum, it's always good to have a rough idea of what the answer should be. This is especially true if you're thumping a load of numbers into a calculator, because if you just miss out one digit you can suddenly get an answer that's miles out without realizing it.

The main secret is to round your numbers off so that the sums become as easy as possible, but still give the closest answer.

We also get to meet a special sign here: "$\approx$" means "roughly equals". In these examples the exact answer is given at the end. (Just a shame that exams don't do that, isn't it?)

Rough adding
$37,945 + 1723 \approx 38,000 + 1700 \approx 39,700$ (= 39,668)
$4988 + 2973 \approx 5000 + 3000 \approx 8000$ (= 7961)

Rough subtracting

$5558 - 3931 \approx 5600 - 4000 \approx 1{,}600$ (= 1627)

$142{,}333 - 116 \approx 142{,}300 - 100 \approx 142{,}200$ (= 142,217)

In the second sum, you might have been tempted to round 142,333 to 140,000 but you've just knocked off 2333 so subtracting another 116 is going to be rather pointless. Obviously, as the first three digits of 142,333 aren't going to be affected by the sum, leave them alone and just concentrate on the $333 - 116$ part of the calculation.

Rough multiplication

If you make a mistake with multiplying or dividing then the error can be far more catastrophic, so let's see how helpful rough sums are here.

> **Suppose you want to send 73 Christmas cards and each one costs 28p. How much will it cost you in total?**

The sum is 73×28 and then you divide by 100 to make pounds and pence. Let's suppose you have a few goes at it and get different answers:

> **a)** £10·36   **b)** £59·86   **c)** £20·44   **d)** £73·28

Before you read on, which do you think is correct?

Now we'll find out with a rough estimate. 73 is near to 70 and 28 is near to 30, so the answer is roughly 70×30 which is 2100. Now divide by 100 and you'll see that the real answer is about £21·00. Answer **c)** £20·44 is likely to be correct.

By the way, look at answer **d)** £73·28. This is a classic mistake with a calculator – you put in 73 and 28 correctly but forgot to push "×" in the middle! It's really silly mistakes like this that always make doing a rough sum worthwhile. Here's another sum:

$719 \times 42 \approx 700 \times 40 \approx 28{,}000 \ (= 30{,}198)$

Notice that both numbers were made smaller, so when multiplied together you should be aware that the estimation will be a bit low.

Rough dividing

$588{,}663 \div 416 \approx 600{,}000 \div 400 \approx 1500 \ (= 1415 \cdot 06)$

$883 \div 0 \cdot 39 \approx 900 \div 0 \cdot 4 \approx 9000 \div 4 \approx 2250 = 2264 \cdot 1)$

Don't be scared by sums like $600{,}000 \div 400$. With divisions you can "divide through" just like fractions. In this case you can divide both numbers by 100 which just leaves $6000 \div 4$.

Dividing by $0 \cdot 4$ might have looked a bit miserable, but again, divisions are like fractions and this time we multiplied through by 10.

Knowing how to get rough estimates quickly is useful for checking all sorts of things, whether it's exam answers or the cost of a load of stuff at the supermarket.

You may well get specific questions on it like these (and keep your fingers off your calculator):

> **1. Round each number in these sums to 1 significant figure, then get a rough answer:**
> **a)** $\frac{31 \cdot 06 - 18 \cdot 2}{2 \cdot 1 + 8 \cdot 4}$ **b)** $317 \cdot 4 \times 40 \cdot 9$
>
> **2. Give approximate answers to:**
> **a)** $3809 \times 31{,}889$ **b)** $0 \cdot 0712 \times 0 \cdot 616$ **c)** $2341 \div 587$
> **d)** $4 \cdot 79 \times 154 \div 0 \cdot 123$

Check these on a calculator after you've come up with your own rough answers. (Rough answers on page 306.)

Positive and negative numbers

Most numbers you deal with are positive, so + 5, + 11 and + 4 are all **positive** numbers. (Usually we don't bother writing the + because we assume a number is positive unless it's marked as a negative.) When you add them together, the total keeps growing.

If you set off to the shops and walked 5 m, then 11 m and then 4 m all in the same direction, you'd end up 20 m away from where you started. This can be shown on a number line.

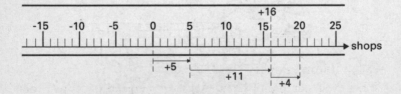

Sometimes you get **negative** numbers such as -3 or -6 or -7. This is a bit like looking towards the shops but walking backwards!

The things I do for my GCSE.

If you set off to the shops and walked -3 m, then -6 m, then -7 m, you'd end up 16 m *further away* from the shops than when you started. You could describe this distance from home as *minus* 16 m or -16 m.

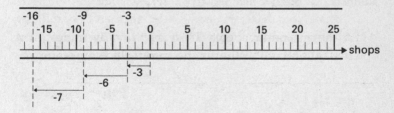

F: Combining positive and negative

When you put positive and negative numbers together, your answer might be either positive or negative. Suppose you are having a really strange day and walk towards the shops in little bursts like this: $+2 - 9 + 11 - 3 - 5$. In total you would have walked + 2 + 11 = + 13 m forwards. BUT you would also have walked – 9 – 3 – 5 = – 17 m backwards. To find out where you finish up you work out + 13 m – 17 m. The way to do sums like 13 – 17 is to take the smaller from the larger (so you work out 17 – 13 = 4), then give the sign of the larger. As 17 was bigger than 13 and it was negative, the final answer is – 4 m. Let's see how it all looks on the number line:

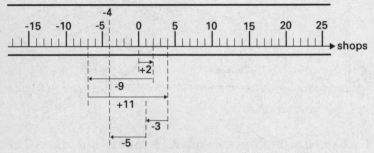

As you can see, if you did these odd little walks in turn you would end up – 4 m nearer the shops, in other words 4 m further away!

Any measurement that can get bigger or smaller uses directed numbers (i.e. positive *and* negative). Try this:

A thermometer shows 7° at midday. By midnight it has fallen by 9°. What is the midnight temperature?

Answer on page 306.

F: Subtracting negative numbers
If you have 6 and subtract 4 you get 2. In figures it's 6 – 4 = 2.

But watch out if you have 6 and subtract *minus* 4. To make the minus 4 clear it might be in a bracket like this: (– 4). In figures this sum is 6 – (– 4) = 10.

If you subtract a negative number, this is the same as adding. In this case – (– 4) is the same as + 4.

To illustrate this, imagine that you've walked 6 steps towards the shops. If you were just going to subtract 4 steps, then you would walk backwards 4 steps. However if you subtract (– 4) steps this is like turning round and *then* walking backwards. Of course this will take you even further towards the shops.

Now I'm getting dizzy!

F: Multiplying and dividing with negative numbers

If you have a number like – 7, you can still multiply by it. To make clear what's going on, people tend to put the – 7 in brackets like this: (– 7). You can then have sums like $4 \times (– 7)$.

Here's how multiplications work out:

positive × positive = positive i.e. $3 \times 6 = + 18$
negative × positive = negative i.e. $(– 2) \times 4 = – 8$
positive × negative = negative i.e. $2 \times (– 10) = – 20$

. . . and strangest of all . . .

negative × negative = positive i.e. $(– 3) \times (– 3) = + 9$

55

> **TOP TIP**
> If the signs are the same, the answer is positive. If the signs are different, the answer is negative.

And now for the good news: the rules are exactly the same for dividing. Here are a few examples: $24 \div 6 = +4$; $(-56) \div 7 = -8$; $81 \div (-9) = -9$; $(-42) \div (-6) = +7$.

Yes, even if you divide a negative number by another negative number, the answer is positive. It's a bit hard to imagine WHY you should ever need to divide a negative by a negative, but in case it ever comes up then you'll know what to do.

F: Powers of negative numbers

Even powers We've just seen that positive × positive = positive, and negative × negative = positive. This means that $5^2 = 25$ and also $(-5)^2 = 25$.

> **The square of any number (positive OR negative) is always positive.**

Odd powers For odd powers the sign stays the same, e.g: $7^3 = 343$ and $(-7)^3 = -343$.

Ratio, scale and proportions

F: Ratio

Just in case you try to escape maths by helping out a bricklayer, you're in for a shock. You have to mix the mortar up and you are told the mixture needs 6 parts sand to 1 part cement. You can say the ratio (or "proportion") of sand to cement is six to one, or in numbers you can write 6:1. In practice you stand by the mixer and shovel in six lots of sand and then one lot of cement. (Don't forget to put in a bit of water too and don't make it too runny. Brickies can get quite stroppy if the stuff splatters all over the place.)

When you've finished you'll have made about 7 shovel-loads of mortar. As 6 of these were sand, the fraction of sand in the mortar is $\frac{6}{7}$. In the same way the amount of cement is $\frac{1}{7}$.

Unfortunately, seven shovel-loads of mortar will only last a decent brickie about two minutes, so you'll need to make bigger quantities. If you put in *twice* the amount of sand, you must also put in *twice* the amount of cement – so you end up with 12 lots of sand and 2 of cement, but the ratio will be the same! You can check this with a fraction – you've now made 14 shovel-loads of mortar and 12 of these are sand. So the fraction of sand in the mortar is $\frac{12}{14}$ which reduces to $\frac{6}{7}$.

If you progress to mixing concrete for foundations, you might put in cement, sand and gravel in the ratio of 1:3:6. You'd end up with 10 loads of concrete and that would include $\frac{1}{10}$ cement, $\frac{3}{10}$ sand and $\frac{6}{10}$ (which is $\frac{3}{5}$) gravel.

WARNING

Sometimes people describe ratios as "proportions". In other words they might say that the proportions of cement to sand in mortar are 1 to 6. This is not strictly accurate as proportion has a slightly different meaning as we'll soon see.

F: Reducing ratios

Suppose there's a big football match with 18,000 Albion supporters and 15,000 City supporters. The ratio of Albion to City fans is 18,000:15,000, but just as with fractions, you should make ratios as low as possible by dividing through with the biggest number that you can. Obviously we can divide through by 1000 first and get 18:15, but then we can divide by 3 to get a ratio of 6:5. So at the match we know that for every six Albion supporters, there are five City supporters.

F: Using ratios

Let's look at a typical exam question:

> **Your school has a 2:3 ratio of girls to boys. If there are 255 people altogether, how many girls and how many boys are there?**

The ratio tells us that $\frac{2}{5}$ of the people are girls and $\frac{3}{5}$ of the people are boys. (Always double-check to make sure you've got this the right way round.) So the number of girls = $\frac{2}{5} \times 255 = 102$ and the number of boys = $\frac{3}{5} \times 255 = 153$. You can check your answer by adding the number of boys and girls: $102 + 153 = 255$.

Time for a bit of practice:

1. Share out £72 in the ratio 1:2:3.

2. The ratios of sheep, ducks and pigs on a farm is 5:3:1. If there are 21 ducks, how many animals are there altogether? How many sheep? How many pigs?

Answers on page 306.

F: Scale

If you want to enlarge or reduce something, you describe how much you're going to change it with the "scale". If you've designed the scenery for a play, you may well have built a small model of the stage. This should be to an accurate "scale" such as 1:10. The model will show every detail of the stage, but it will be ten times smaller. If your model showed a doorway to be 20 cm high, then to see how big the real doorway should be you multiply 20 cm × 10. The real doorway will be 200 cm high.

TOP TIP

When you use scales, the trick is to use your common sense and decide if your answer should be bigger or smaller. That way you can check if you should be multiplying or dividing.

You might want to build a small scale model of your lovely self and you choose a scale of 1:5. If you are 150 cm tall – how tall should the model be? Common-sense time – obviously the model should be *smaller* – so you divide the 150 cm by 5. It works out that your model would be 30 cm tall.

Of course you might be *so* lovely that they want you to make a giant model of yourself to go in Trafalgar Square. In this case you might choose a scale of 20:1. (Putting the 20 first would usually indicate that you are going to enlarge something – in this case yourself.) Here the model will be larger so you multiply your height by 20. The model will turn out to be 30 m tall and it will scare everybody to bits.

Maps always use a scale, such as 1:100,000. If two villages are 7 cm apart on a map with this scale, then in real life the distance between them would be 7 cm × 100,000. This works out to be 700,000 cm which is the same as 7 km. (We'll look at things like centimetres and kilometres later.)

I: What are proportions?

If you go to the shops and buy twice as many things as you need, then you'll spend twice as much money. That's because the amount you spend is in *direct proportion* to the amount you get. There's a sign for this. If "S" is what you spend and "G" is what you get then: $S \propto G$.

Suppose a gang of you are buying a present for someone. The more people there are to split the cost, then the less each person will have to pay. This is called *inverse proportion*. If "P" is what each person pays and "N" is how many people are paying then: $P \propto \frac{1}{N}$.

TOP TIP
Make absolutely sure you know whether you are dealing with direct or inverse proportions.
- If one thing getting bigger makes the other get bigger – that's direct.
- If one thing getting bigger makes the other get smaller – that's inverse.

Let's see how these two things come up.

I: Direct proportions

Suppose you've got two numbers A and B that are proportional, then $A \propto B$. If you multiply A by any number, then you have to multiply B by the same number. The ratio of A:B is always the same, no matter how big or small A and B become.

Here's an example of what you might be asked in an exam:

A is directly proportional to B and A = 2 when B = 7.
a) Find A when B = 21   **b)** Find B when A = 1

It can help to draw out a little table:

A: 2 a 1
B: 7   21 b

Think of it like this: the first column shows that to start with A = 2 when B = 7. As you move to the second column you see that B has changed from 7 to become 21. B has been multiplied by $\frac{21}{7}$ = 3, so to see what number should go in the space marked "a" we have to multiply the start value of A by 3. We get $2 \times 3 = 6$.

Ignore the middle column now and look at the first and last columns. You'll see that A has gone from 2 to 1 so it has been divided by 2. So to get the "b" value, we divide 7 by 2 and get the answer $3\frac{1}{2}$.

A car uses 15 litres of petrol to go 240 km. How far will it travel with 25 litres? If you wanted to go 170 km, how much fuel would you need?

Here's a suitable table:

Distance: 240 x 170
Fuel: 15   25 y

"x" is how far it will travel with 25 litres and "y" is the amount of fuel needed for 170 km.

In the first two columns, the fuel has gone from 15 to 25 so it has been multiplied by $\frac{25}{15}$. Therefore if we multiply the distance in the first column by $\frac{25}{15}$ we get: $x = 240 \times \frac{25}{15} = 400$ km.

You can check this with your common sense: as you are using more fuel, the answer must be bigger than 240 km. If it wasn't then you should go back and see what's wrong!

What do you get for "y"? (Answer on page 306.)

H: Inverse proportions

If C and D are in "inverse proportion" then $C \propto \frac{1}{D}$. If C gets multiplied by 2 then D gets divided by 2 and vice versa. Here's a typical exam question:

> **C is inversely proportional to D and C = 5 when D = 3.**
> **a)** Find C when D = 12   **b)** Find D when C = 7

Let's do a table again:

C:	5	c	7
D:	3	12	d

This time we've got to think: D started off by being 3 but to become 12 it had to be multiplied by 4. Therefore C must be divided by 4. As C started off as 5, the value for "c" on the table is $5 \div 4 = 1\frac{1}{4}$. What do you get for "d"? (Answer on page 306.)

> **If you run at 10 km/h it will take you 35 minutes to get round town. How long would the same journey take you if you ran at 12 km/h? What speed would you need to go if you wanted to run it in 20 minutes?**

Speed and time are inversely proportional because if you go twice as fast the same journey takes half the time. Again you can set the results out in a table with "s" and "t" being the two answers you need:

Speed:	10	12	s
Time:	35	t	20

Your turn, and check the answers with your common sense! E.g. if you run faster, your time will be less. (Answers on page 307.)

63

H: Inverse squares

You are standing 10 metres from a bonfire but find it's too hot, so you move back to 20 metres. Although you have doubled the distance, you will find you are only feeling $\frac{1}{4}$ of the heat from the bonfire that you felt previously. This is one of the many things in physics and maths that obeys the *inverse square* law. The most famous example is Isaac Newton's law of gravity which says that the force of attraction between two objects is *inversely proportional to the square of the distance between them*.

In terms of maths, if "f" is the force of attraction and "d" is the distance between the two objects, then $f \propto \frac{1}{d^2}$. Let's look at a question:

The force of attraction between two asteroids is 100 Newtons. What would the force be if the two asteroids were 3 times further apart?

We can write a little table, but we'll put in an extra line for the distance squared. "f" is the force we are trying to find, and as we don't know what distance the asteroids are apart to start with, we'll just call it "d". When we move them 3 times further apart, this distance becomes $3 \times d$ or $3d$ for short.

Force:	100	f
Distance:	d	$3d$
Distance squared:	d^2	$9d^2$

Ignore the "distance" line of the table because it's distance squared we're concerned with here. To get from the first column to the second, d^2 has been multiplied by 9. As it's an inverse law, this means the force in the first column must be divided by 9 to give the result marked f in the second column. So: $f = 100 \div 9 = 11 \cdot 11$ Newtons.

64

Suppose you had the same two asteroids, but the distance between them was halved. What would the force be?

Answer on page 307.

Accuracy
I: Discrete and continuous measurements

Suppose you've got 28 goldfish in a bowl sucking the green stuff off the glass.

The number of goldfish is a **discrete measurement** because you can say exactly how many fish there are. There cannot be 28·06 or 27·91 goldfish, it has to be 28. If you put in 3 more fish, the total will switch straight up to 31.

However the weight of the goldfish is a **continuous measurement** because you can't give it absolutely accurately. If you are told they weigh 291 g in total, would you think it's *exactly* 291 g – in other words 291·0000000 g? Of course not. What's more, as they eat the green stuff their weight will gradually go up.

This green stuff stinks!

When measurements are continuous, it's important to know how accurate they are. (Well, it is if you want to get any marks in this bit of the exams.)

I: Upper and lower bounds

We've already seen how to round off measurements and we've found out what significant digits are. If somebody passes you a sack and says it holds 34 kg of carrots, unless you're told otherwise, you can assume it was weighed to the nearest kg. That means the sack could hold anything between 33·5 and 34·5 kg. These two values are called the **upper** and **lower bounds**. In this case the upper bound is 0·5 kg more than 34 kg, and the lower bound is 0·5 kg less than 34 kg.

You could say the sack weighs 34 kg *give or take half a kilogram*. In maths we'd write it like this: 34 ± 0·5 kg. The "±" sign means "plus or minus". If you add the 0·5 kg you get the maximum weight and if you subtract the 0·5 kg you get the minimum weight of the sack.

Quite often you are told that a measurement is made to the "nearest kg" or "nearest cm" or even the "nearest 0·5". You have to be able to work out what the upper and lower bounds are.

Suppose you are given a measurement of 800 cm to the nearest cm, then you divide whatever the "nearest" unit is by 2. In this case the nearest unit is 1 cm so you know that the exact measurement comes somewhere in between 800 ± $\frac{1}{2}$ cm (or in decimals: 800 ± 0·5 cm). It only takes a very simple pair of sums to see that the lower bound is 799·5 cm and the upper bound is 800·5 cm. Have a look at this on a ruler:

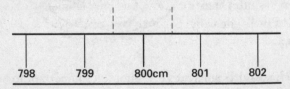

Any length that falls between the dotted lines could be called 800 ± 0·5 cm.

What if you're given a distance such as 22 km to the nearest 0·5 km? As the "nearest" bit is 0·5 km then you divide it by 2 to get 0·25 km. You then know that the upper and lower bounds of the distance are 22 ± 0·25 km. The maximum is therefore 22·25 km and the minimum is 21·75 km.

I: Assuming accuracy

As we've just seen, sometimes you are told how accurate a measurement or number is, and other times you are not. If you are not told, then you have to decide for yourself how accurate it is.

Usually you would assume a measurement is accurate to the last given digit, so if a journey is 127 km, you'd assume it was accurate to the nearest 1 km. However, life gets trickier when there are zeros about the place. If somebody tells you they have just jogged 800 m, they probably mean to the nearest 100 m – in other words they could have gone anywhere between 750 m and 850 m. But if they actually say they've jogged "800 m to the nearest 5 m" then you know it's somewhere between 797·5 m and 802·5 m. This could be written as 800 ± 2·5 m .

Decimals have their own way of showing their accuracy. If a worm is measured as 9·38 cm long, then you would assume it is accurate down to 0·01 cm, i.e. the worm is between 9·375 cm and 9·385 cm long. However, if the worm is measured as 9·380 cm long then that extra zero indicates the measurement is accurate to 0·001 cm – so the worm could be between 9·3795 and 9·3805 cm.

I: Adding with accuracy

You are given 10 sacks of carrots, all weighed at 34 kg. What is the maximum or minimum they could weigh?

67

You need to do two sums to work this sort of thing out:

- First you suppose all the sacks happened to be the maximum weight of 34·5 kg. Then the 10 sacks would weigh 10 × 34·5 kg = 345 kg.
- Then you suppose they were all the minimum weight so they would weigh 10 × 33·5 kg = 335 kg.

H: Multiplying with accuracy (areas and volumes)

When we multiplied 10 sacks of carrots, although the weight of the sacks may have varied a bit, at least we knew the number 10 was exactly 10. Things get a bit trickier if you are multiplying two numbers which can both vary.

If you want to work out the area of a rectangle, then you multiply the length by the width. Let's say the length is 35 cm and the width is 25 cm and we'll assume these lengths are given to the nearest cm. Using these values, we'd get an area of 35 × 25 = 875 cm^2.

To get the maximum area, we need to multiply the two upper bounds of the measurements which are 35·5 cm × 25·5 cm = 905·25 cm^2. To get the minimum area we'd use the lower bounds and get 34·5 cm × 24·5 cm = 845·25 cm^2.

Volumes work the same way – you have to work out what the upper bounds of each measurement are, then multiply them to get the maximum volume. Then work out all the lower bounds and multiply them to get the minimum. Try this one yourself:

> **A rectangular swimming pool measures 12 m × 25 m and is 2·2 m deep. What are the maximum and minimum volumes to the nearest m^3?**

Answers on page 307.

H: Percentage error

If you said that your sofa weighs 130 kg ± 5 kg, then 5 kg is the maximum error. You can make this into a percentage with this formula:

$$\text{Percentage error} = \frac{\text{maximum error}}{\text{average value}} \times 100$$

In this case we'd get $\frac{5}{130} \times 100 = 3 \cdot 85\%$ error.

This also works the other way round. Suppose the milometer on your Rolls Royce reads "87225" and you know that it is accurate to 2%. What is the highest distance it might have travelled? You work out the maximum error which is $\frac{2}{100} \times 87{,}225$ and this comes to 1744·5. Add this to the reading you have and you get $87{,}225 + 1744 \cdot 5 = 88{,}969 \cdot 5$.

Rational and irrational numbers

What are they?

H: We know that $3 \times 3 = 3^2 = 9$ and therefore $\sqrt{9} = 3$. If a number is itself a "square", then it will have a whole number as a square root. The smallest squares are 1, 4, 9, 16, 25, 36 . . . and these come from $1^2, 2^2, 3^2, 4^2, 5^2, 6^2$ ... So $\sqrt{1} = 1, \sqrt{4} = 2, \sqrt{9} = 3, \sqrt{16} = 4, \sqrt{25} = 5, \sqrt{36} = 6$.

But what about $\sqrt{2}$? Here we want to know what number multiplied by itself makes 2. It isn't 1, because $1^2 = 1$ which is too small, and it isn't 2 because $2^2 = 4$ which is too big. The answer must be somewhere between 1 and 2.

How about 1·5? No, because $1·5 \times 1·5 = 2·25$.

Maybe 1·4 will do it? Sadly not, because $1·4 \times 1·4 = 1·96$.

It turns out that the answer is 1·4142135... and the row of dots tells you that the list of digits goes on for *ever* in a completely unpredictable pattern. The amazing fact is that it is impossible to write down the exact value of $\sqrt{2}$. Numbers like this are called **irrational numbers** or sometimes **surds** and there are tons of them. The square root of any number that is not a perfect square is irrational such as $\sqrt{3}, \sqrt{5}, \sqrt{6}, \sqrt{7}, \sqrt{8}, \sqrt{10}$ and so on.

Which of the following are rational numbers?
1·2   3·14 π $\frac{\pi}{2}$ $\sqrt{\frac{4}{9}}$ $\sqrt{11}$ $(4·2)^3$

Answer on page 307.

H: Sorting out surds

"Surds" sound vaguely unhygienic, and you'd be forgiven for thinking they must be one of the most miserable subjects in maths. That's a shame because there's not much to them and once you've learnt the basic procedure it should give you a couple of easy marks in your exam. Maybe if they were called "twinkles" it would be more obvious that it's quite a jolly little subject. Anyway, let's have a look at them. . .

Surds are a bit like shellfish. You can imagine that nasty little square root sign as a shell, and if you're lucky you can get a pin and prise most of the insides out. Have a look at $\sqrt{8}$. Instead of writing "8" we could put "4 × 2" because 4 × 2 = 8. Therefore $\sqrt{8} = \sqrt{4 \times 2}$ We can go a bit further because it turns out that $\sqrt{4 \times 2} = \sqrt{4} \times \sqrt{2}$. This is getting exciting because if you're sharp you'll realize that $\sqrt{4} = 2$ and so we can say that $\sqrt{8} = 2 \times \sqrt{2} = 2\sqrt{2}$. (You can miss the "×" sign out of things like this. When it comes to working them out you just assume everything is multiplied together.) In other words, the surd of 8 is just 2 × the surd of 2. It's much nicer just to be left with a little "2" inside the square root sign instead of the big floppy "8" we started with.

Here are the general rules for sorting out surds:

- See if the number inside the root sign will divide by a perfect square. If you've got $\sqrt{18}$, then it turns out that 18 will divide by 9 which is 3^2.
- Move the square to the outside of the root sign. Here you do this by dividing the 18 by 9, leaving 2 inside the sign. As the 9 moves outside, it becomes 3. (This is because $\sqrt{9} = 3$, so 9 inside a root sign becomes 3 outside it.) You end up with $\sqrt{18} = 3\sqrt{2}$.

You'll see that most of the number inside the square root sign has been prised out leaving the smallest irrational number possible inside.

Simplify these square roots: a) $\sqrt{20}$ **b)** $\sqrt{72}$ **c)** $\sqrt{96}$

Answers on page 307.

Once you've got the hang of this, then sums like these are simple: $\sqrt{48} - \sqrt{27} = 4\sqrt{3} - 3\sqrt{3} = \sqrt{3}$. You'll see that we could take 4^2 out of the $\sqrt{48}$ (because 48 will divide by 16) and 3^2 out of the $\sqrt{27}$

(because 27 will divide by 9). We ended up with four "root threes" minus three "root threes" which just left one "root three" by itself.

H: Getting rid of irrational numbers

If you just have one irrational number by itself in a sum, such as $\sqrt{5}$, then you'll never get rid of it. However, if you have two of the same irrational number and manage to multiply them together, then they will disappear and produce a **rational** number for you. E.g. $\sqrt{5} \times \sqrt{5} = \sqrt{5^2} = 5$.

$\sqrt{5} \times \sqrt{5}$ is NOT the same as $2 \times \sqrt{5}$. It's a simple trap to fall into, but $\sqrt{5} = 2 \cdot 2360679\ldots$ so multiplying by this number is not the same as multiplying by 2.

OK . . . it's calculator time

Hopefully you've managed to keep your hands off the calculator so far, but now it's time to see what we need it to do for us.

Your calculator should have all these buttons:

And if you're going for Intermediate or Higher level you need:

- sin, cos, tan and also $\sin^{-1}, \cos^{-1}, \tan^{-1}$
- STAT or SD (see the Standard Deviation section)

Just about any "scientific" calculator will have this lot, but it's worth checking. You shouldn't need to spend more than about £7, and it's probably a good idea NOT to buy something with trillions of buttons you don't need.

TURBO CALCULATOR

TOP TIP
Make sure you can work it! Different makes of calculator expect you to push the buttons in different ways, and the symbols on the keys can also be different. So another vital tip is: only use your OWN calculator.

Calculators can do difficult sums for you, but only if you tell them exactly what you want them to do. It's no good blaming a calculator for a wrong answer because, funnily enough, they are too stupid to give wrong answers! If a calculator gives you the wrong answer, it's because you have asked it the wrong question.

Standard index form

This is a way of dealing with extremely big (or extremely tiny) numbers, so that you avoid tons and tons of zeros all over the place. Your calculator will convert numbers into SI form automatically. For example if you put in a sum such as 87654321 × 987654321 the answer will be too big to appear in full on your screen, so you might get:

Or if your calculator is posh:

Although they are all slightly different, they are all giving the same answer in standard form which is to have the first digit, then a decimal point, then some decimals followed by an Exponential, in other words a power of 10. In this case you could convert $8.65721689 \times 10^{16}$ by moving the point 16 places to the *right* and get an answer of 86572168900000000. This is rather messy, and besides, the calculator rounded off the last few digits so it is not absolutely accurate – which makes all those zeros rather pointless. You also have to count them all up to see how big the number is, but if you just look at 10^{16} you get a pretty good idea of the size straight away.

How about a sum such as 1 ÷ 987654321? Your calculator might show the answer as $1 \cdot 012499999^{-9}$ or 1·012499999 E –9. To work out the real value you move the decimal point 9 places to the *left* (because of the minus sign). You would get 0·000000001012499999 which is rather ugly.

If you have to convert numbers to standard form, then all you do is move the decimal point and count how many places you've moved it.

Suppose you had to convert 3460000 to SI form:

- Imagine where the decimal point is to start with (3460000 = 3460000·0).
- Move the point along until it comes after the first digit (3·460000) and count how many places you've moved it. In this case it's 6 places to the left.
- The number of places is the index number, so you get $3 \cdot 46 \times 10^6$.

TOP TIP
You should always write SI form as $3 \cdot 46 \times 10^6$ and NOT as a calculator might write it, e.g. 3·46 E6.

Don't forget: with fractions you're moving the point the other way, so the index number is negative. 0·0000678 becomes $6 \cdot 78 \times 10^{-5}$.

TOP TIP

Remember, the decimal point comes after the FIRST digit.

These are NOT SI form: $561 \cdot 0 \times 10^4$, $0 \cdot 324 \times 10^{-6}$, $7298 \cdot 0 \times 10^{-11}$. Can you see what they should be? (Answers on page 307.)

If you need to put a number such as $2 \cdot 47 \times 10^9$ into your calculator, you need to find the "exponent" button which will be marked EXP or E or EE. You then type in $2 \cdot 47$ [EXP] 9 and you should see the number correctly displayed.

Just while we're on the subject, we know that $10^1 = 10$ and $10^{-1} = \frac{1}{10}$ or $0 \cdot 1$. In between the two comes $10^0 = 1$. In fact *any* number to the power of 0 equals 1.

I: Multiplying and dividing with SI form

You would normally do these with a calculator, but you should know what's going on. Here are some examples:

$$(3 \times 10^5) \times (6 \times 10^7)$$

- First you multiply: $3 \times 6 = 18$
- Next you ADD the index numbers. $10^5 \times 10^7 = 10^{12}$
- Put them together and get the answer 18×10^{12} . . . but this is NOT standard form!
- Move the decimal point one place and get $1 \cdot 8 \times 10^{13}$

With a calculator you'd enter: 3 [EXP] 5 × 6 [EXP] 7 = and you'd get $1 \cdot 8 \times 10^{13}$.

$$(4 \times 10^{15}) \div (8 \times 10^{11})$$

- Divide: $4 \div 8 = 0.5$
- As we are dividing we *subtract* the indices so $10^{15} \div 10^{11} = 10^4$
- Put them together and get 0.5×10^4
- Convert to standard form and get 5×10^3

On the calculator: 4 [EXP] 15 ÷ 8 [EXP] 11 = 5×10^3 (or 5000).

If there are negative indices around then you have to be extra careful. . .

$$(9.0 \times 10^{13}) \times (6.0 \times 10^{-6})$$

When you add the indices you're adding (+ 13) to (− 6) which makes 7. Your answer should be 36×10^7 which converts to 3.6×10^8.

$$(6.0 \times 10^{11}) \div (2.0 \times 10^{-7})$$

Here we are subtracting the indices, so it's (+ 11) − (− 7). Remember that when you subtract a negative number, you really add it on. Our final answer is 3×10^{18}.

$$(1.0 \times 10^{-4}) \div (4.0 \times 10^{-7})$$

Cheer up, this is as miserable as it gets! This time the indices give us (− 4) − (− 7). This is the same as − 4 + 7, which makes 3. The answer is 0.25×10^3 which becomes 2.5×10^2 or 250 in normal numbers.

I: Adding and subtracting with SI form
If the numbers have the same indices then adding and subtracting

are easy. All you do is add or subtract the digits and keep the same power of ten. So $(4 \times 10^7) + (9 \times 10^7) = 13 \times 10^7 = 1.3 \times 10^8$ and $(8 \times 10^{43}) - (3 \times 10^{43}) = 5 \times 10^{43}$.

When the indices are different you have two choices:

- You can convert everything into ordinary numbers and do the sum.
- You can convert one number to have the same index as the other.

Let's try one:

$$(6 \times 10^5) - (9 \times 10^3)$$

We'll convert it to ordinary numbers and get $600000 - 9000 = 591000$ and then we can convert this back to 5.91×10^5.

Otherwise we'll change the (9×10^3) into (0.09×10^5). We then work out $(6 - 0.09) \times 10^5 = 5.91 \times 10^5$.

As long as you keep careful count of the zeros, for indices up to about 6 you'll find it's easier to use normal numbers. However, if you're unlucky enough to get a sum like $(8 \times 10^{15}) + (7 \times 10^{17})$ you're better off converting. Try working this one out for yourself. Go on, you know you want to. (Answer on page 307.)

I: Reciprocals

Look at this: $69 \div 23 = 69 \times \frac{1}{23}$.

If you need to divide by a number, this is the same as "turning it upside down" and multiplying. You can imagine any number as being "over 1" so for example 7 is the same as $\frac{7}{1}$. If you need to divide by 7, you turn it upside down and multiply, so $\div 7$ would become $\times \frac{1}{7}$. You would say that $\frac{1}{7}$ is the **reciprocal** of 7.

Quite often you need the reciprocal of a number on a calculator, so use the $[\frac{1}{x}]$ button. This often comes up in conversions. For instance, if you know that 1 pound = 0·45 kg, then how many pounds make 1 kg? The answer is $\frac{1}{0.45}$, so if you put 0·45 $[\frac{1}{x}]$ into the calculator you'll get 2·22 which is correct.

Compound measures
Some things need two completely different sorts of measurements put together.

F: Speed
Speed needs a combination of two units. One is a distance and one is a time, and that's why speed might be measured in kilometres per hour or metres per second.

Remember that, in maths, "per" means "divided by". This gives you a clue how to work things like speed out. With kilometres per hour, you need to know the distance travelled in kilometres and then divide it by the time in hours.

TOP TIP
It's extra important to make sure you're using the right units for compound measures.

$$\text{Speed (in kilometres per hour)} = \frac{\text{Distance (in kilometres)}}{\text{Time (in hours)}}$$

If your mate Sidney tells you that he's just run 8 kilometres in 10 minutes, you could work out his speed in kilometres per hour, which would be written km/h.

The first thing to do is convert your measurements into the units you want. The distance is already in kilometres so that's OK, but the time is in minutes so you need to convert it to hours. There are 60 minutes in an hour, but do we multiply or divide by 60? Because we know that 10 minutes is a small part of one hour, the answer we want is small, so DIVIDE by 60. We get 10 minutes $= \frac{10}{60}$ hours $= 0\cdot167$ h.

We can now put the numbers into the speed formula: Sidney's speed = distance ÷ time $= 8 \div \frac{10}{60} = 8 \times \frac{60}{10} = 48$ km/h. So you can tell Sidney that his speed is 48 km/h. You can also tell him that he was lying because nobody runs that fast.

The fastest runners do 100 metres in about 10 seconds, which puts their speed at $\frac{100}{10} = 10$ m/s. What's that in km/h?

If your speed is 10 m/s, you'll travel 10 metres in 1 second. There are 60 × 60 seconds in an hour which works out to 3600 seconds. So in 1 hour, you'll travel 10 × 3600 metres. That's 36,000m which is 36 km. So 10 m/s is the same as 36 km/hour.

Because Speed = Distance ÷ Time, if you know any two of the

measurements, then you can work out the third by adjusting the formula:

Speed × Time = Distance $$\text{Time} = \frac{\text{Distance}}{\text{Speed}}$$

Your uncle tows his caravan at 25 km/h for six hours in the middle of the M1. How many miles does he travel?

We know the speed and time so: distance = 25 km/h × 6 h = 150 km.

When he finally stopped, he was 15 km from the nearest police car which rushed to get him at 120 km/h. How long did the police car take to arrive?

Time = Distance/Speed = $\frac{15}{120}$ = 0·125 . . . er, whoops! What units are we using? Distance was in km and the speed was in km/h, so the time will be 0·125 hours. Let's convert this to minutes – there are 60 minutes in an hour, so our answer will be a bigger number, so *multiply* 0·125 × 60 = 7·5 minutes.

TOP TIP
Always remember the units, otherwise you may throw away a mark.

F: Density

This also needs two different units. One is mass and the other is volume. Water has a density of 1000 kg per cubic metre or 1000 kg/m^3. This gives us the clue that the density formula is:

$$\text{Density} = \frac{\text{Mass}}{\text{Volume}}$$

So if you have a block of concrete measuring 80 cm × 50 cm × 40 cm with a mass of 200 kg, you can work out the density of the concrete. First we need to know the volume of the block in cubic metres (or m^3). We need to convert all the measurements to metres and we get 0·8 × 0·5 × 0·4 = 0·16 m^3. Now we can put the numbers in: density in kg/m^3 = $\frac{200}{0·16}$ = 1250 kg/m^3.

Just like speed, if you know two of the measurements you can work out the third.

> **Solid gold has a density of 19·3 g/cm^3. You happen to find a lump measuring 25 cm × 20 cm × 15 cm. Could you carry it home?**
>
> $$\text{Density} = \frac{\text{Mass}}{\text{Volume}} \quad \text{So Mass} = \text{Density} \times \text{Volume}$$

First work out the volume of the gold: 25 × 20 × 15 = 7500 cm^3. The mass of the gold lump will be 7500 × 19·3 = 144750 g or 144·75 kg. (There are a thousand grams in a kilogram.) It turns out the lump weighs more than twice as much as you, so be careful!

I think I'm allergic to Algebra!

F: Introduction and some useful words

People who don't know much maths often think it just involves numbers, a few triangles and the odd graph or two.

You mean it doesn't?

So when they see equations using letters, such as $x^2 + 3y = 4$, it all looks immensely complicated and mysterious. Of course it's nothing like that. The letters are just a convenient way of showing what sums you need to do when you don't know what numbers are involved.

Algebra arrives on your exam paper in three basic forms:

- Formulae
- Equations
- Graphs

Algebra has a few words that you need to get the hang of:

Variables   These are letters (or other symbols) which represent numbers that you might not know, or that might change.

Constants   These are numbers or letters with a fixed value.

Expression   This is a collection of numbers and letters arranged together with signs like + − × ÷ and brackets.

Here's an example of all these: the area of a label needed to go round a cylinder (such as a tin of beans) is given by the *expression* $2\pi rh$. This expression works for any size of cylinder, so let's take it apart and see what it means.

2 is just the number 2 and is a constant.

π is a symbol that always represents 3·141593... so it is also a constant. (This peculiar number comes up a great deal in maths so having this little sign saves hours of having to write it out.)

r is the radius of the base of the cylinder and is a variable. For a thin cylinder it would be a small measurement, for a fat cylinder it would be bigger.

h is the height of the cylinder and is also a variable.

radius = r

When all the constants and variables are clumped together with no space between them it just means they are all multiplied together. If the radius was 4 cm and the height was 10 cm, then the area would be 2 × π × 4 × 10. You could bang all this into a calculator and find the area is 251·3 cm^2.

If you wanted a round label for the top, the expression for the area would be πr^2 and, as you might expect, $r^2 = r \times r$.

Sometimes you get expressions like this: $5x - 4xy - 7x^2 - 3x + 4x^2$.

And for this sort of thing there are more handy words.

Term   Each little bit with its own + or − sign is a separate term. This expression has five terms.

Coefficient This is the number in front of a term, so if you have $7r^3$ then 7 is the coefficient of r^3.

Like terms These terms have exactly the same combination of letters. In this case the $5x$ and $-3x$ are "like terms". So are the $-7x^2$ and $+4x^2$.

Simplification You can do mini sums with like terms by adding or subtracting the coefficients such as $5x - 3x = 2x$. Also $-7x^2 + 4x^2 = -3x^2$. This means the expression $5x - 4xy - 7x^2 - 3x + 4x^2$ can be simplified to $2x - 3x^2 - 4xy$.

TOP TIP

You should always simplify answers when you can. Unless you're especially asked to, don't leave any like terms in an expression such as: $2a^2 - 3b + 2a^2 + 6b - ab$. Simplify it and get $4a^2 + 3b - ab$.

F: Multiplying and dividing with algebra

It's easiest to look at some examples and see what's going on:

$a \times b = ab$ This is easy. If you multiply two different letters together, you just write them next to each other.

$-3a \times 5b = -15ab$ With numbers and letters, you multiply the numbers and put the letters together.

$-a^4 \times -6a^2 = 6a^6$

When you multiply $a^4 \times a^2$ you just add the indices and get a^6. (Note: minus times minus makes a plus!)

$\frac{20d^3}{4d} = 20d^3 \div 4d = 5d^2$

For dividing you subtract the indices.

$m^{-2} = \frac{1}{m^2}$

A negative index just means "one over" or "the reciprocal of".

$\frac{12p^2q}{-3pr^2} = \frac{-4pq}{r^2}$

You'll notice that the p on the bottom will divide into the p^2 on top but otherwise none of the other letters will simplify. (Note: plus divided by minus gives a minus.)

F: Expanding (getting rid of brackets)

Brackets tell you when to treat a bunch of terms all the same.

$2t(1 + 4y) = 2t + 8yt$

This tells you that you have to multiply the 1 by $2t$ and also multiply the $4y$ by $2t$. In other words, you must multiply the $2t$ by *everything* inside the brackets.

$-(p - 2q) = -p + 2q$

The $-$ sign outside the brackets means multiply the insides by -1. That's why $-2q$ inside the bracket became $+2q$ outside.

$(rst)^2 = r^2s^2t^2$

The brackets tell you that *everything* inside them is squared, which gives $r \times r \times s \times s \times t \times t$. If you didn't have the

87

brackets and just had rst^2 then that would be $r \times s \times t \times t$.

$\frac{(p-6)}{3} = \frac{p}{3} - \frac{6}{3} = \frac{p}{3} - 2$ The brackets show that both terms must be divided by 3.

$(a + 3b)^2 = (a + 3b)(a + 3b)$ Here you must make sure you multiply
$= a(a + 3b) + 3b(a + 3b)$ *everything* in the first bracket by
$= a^2 + 3ab + 3ab + 9b^2$ *everything* in the second bracket.
$= a^2 + 6ab + 9b^2$

Watch out! $(a + 3b)^2$ is NOT the same as $(a)^2 + (3b)^2$. You must multiply the brackets out completely!

To illustrate this, we'll put in some numbers for a and b. Let's suppose $a = 2$ and $b = 3$.

$(a + 3b)^2 = (2 + 3 \times 3)^2 = (2 + 9)^2 = (11)^2 = 121$

$(a)^2 + (3b)^2 = (2)^2 + (3 \times 3)^2 = (2)^2 + (9)^2 = 4 + 81 = 85$

As you can see, $(a + 3b)^2$ and $(a)^2 + (3b)^2$ give very different results.

Let's expand another and see what it looks like:

$\frac{(a + 2)(3 - a)}{2} = \frac{a(3 - a) + 2(3 - a)}{2} = \frac{3a - a^2 + 6 - 2a}{2}$

(Note: get rid of the brackets completely before any dividing.)

$= \frac{a - a^2 + 6}{2} = \frac{a}{2} - \frac{a^2}{2} + 3$ That's as far as it goes.

When you have fractions such as $\frac{3m+4}{5}$ or $\frac{2}{n-6}$ you have to treat the tops and bottoms as if they were in brackets. Be especially careful when there are one or more brackets on the bottom because although you can do: $\frac{3m+4}{5} = \frac{3m}{5} + \frac{4}{5}$ you CANNOT do this: $\frac{2}{n-6} = \frac{2}{n} - \frac{2}{6}$

Time for you to have a go:

> **Expand the following expressions: a)** $4p(3p + 2)$
> **b)** $(y + 4)(2y - 1)$ **c)** $(1 + q)(2 - 3q)$ **d)** $(3r + s)(1 - 2s)$

Answers on page 307.

Factorizing (putting things into brackets)

When you get rid of brackets by multiplying everything out, it's called **expanding**. The opposite of this is putting things back into brackets and this is called **factorizing**.

If you get something like $3x^2 + 12x$, you need to see if there is anything that will divide into both terms. Here you'll find that both terms will divide by $3x$ so that's what you do: $3x^2 + 12x = 3x(x + 4)$.

> **TOP TIP**
> Always check factorizations by multiplying them out again to see if you're right.

Here's another: $2a^2b - 6ab^3 = 2(a^2b - 3ab^3) = 2a(ab - 3b^3) = 2ab(a - 3b^2)$. We've done this one bit by bit. First the 2 is taken out, then the a and finally the b. Of course you could have been clever and taken the $2ab$ out all at once, but if you're not completely confident, there's no harm in taking it steadily. If you make a mistake it's easier to spot and it also lets the examiners see what you were doing. They like that.

Aaaah! I can really see how this student's mind works!

Right, your go:

Factorize the following: a) $3a + ab$ **b)** $4pq + 2q^2$
c) $2c - 4c^2$ **d)** $3a - b^2$

Answers on page 307.

I: Quadratics

One special form of factorization involves expressions that look like this: $x^2 + 7x + 6$; or $x^2 - 6x + 8$; or $x^2 - x - 20$; or $x^2 + 3x - 18$.

- Quadratic expressions only use one letter.
- The biggest power is a "square".

Before you go on, look at the signs then choose one of these options:

When both signs are +

$x^2 + 7x + 6$ The plan is to factorize the expression into two brackets like this $(x + \quad)(x + \quad)$ and the clever bit is knowing what to put in the gaps.

First you look at the constant at the end and see what factors it has. In this case we look at the 6, which can either come from 3×2 or 6×1. We need two factors that ADD to make the number in the middle, so the 3×2 is no good but the 6×1 will do because $6 + 1 = 7$. This means we can put the 6 and the 1 into the brackets and get $(x + 6)(x + 1)$. Let's multiply this out to test it: $(x + 6)(x + 1) = x^2 + 6x + x + 6 = x^2 + 7x + 6$. It works. Terrific.

When the middle sign is − and the end sign is +

$x^2 − 6x + 8$ You use exactly the same process as before except that the two brackets will BOTH have − signs like this $(x − \quad)(x − \quad)$.

The constant is 8 and can either come from 4×2 or 8×1. In this case $4 + 2$ makes the 6 we need for the middle so we just plonk them in and get $(x − 4)(x − 2)$. Time to test it . . . $(x − 4)(x − 2) = x^2 − 4x − 2x + 8 = x^2 − 6x + 8$. Lovely.

When both signs are −

$x^2 − x − 20$ Here we'll end up with one + bracket and one − bracket like this: $(x + \quad)(x − \quad)$. There's a slight change of plan here because when we look at the factors which make the constant, they need to SUBTRACT to make the number in the middle.

The number in the middle is − 1 so what we need are two factors of 20 that subtract to make − 1. As $5 \times 4 = 20$, we can use $4 − 5 = − 1$. Let's put them in and see what we get: $(x + 4)(x − 5) = x^2 − 5x + 4x − 20 = x^2 − x − 20$. Nice one. (Note: the *bigger* factor goes in the bracket with the − sign.)

When the middle sign is + and the end sign is −

$x^2 + 3x - 18$ This is the same as when both signs are −, the only difference being that the *smaller* factor goes in the bracket with the − sign.

Go on, it's your turn, you work it out. (Answer on page 308.)

TOP TIP

If the constant sign is + then ADD the factors to make the x coefficient. If the constant sign is − then SUBTRACT the factors to make the x coefficient.

To sum up the four variations:

Signs	Brackets	*What the factors of the constant need to do to make the middle number (the "x" coefficient)*
+ +	$(x +\ )(x +\ )$	add together
− +	$(x -\ )(x -\ )$	add together
− −	$(x +\ )(x -\ )$	subtract (bigger factor gets − sign)
+ −	$(x +\ )(x -\ )$	subtract (bigger factor gets + sign)

It's time you had a bit of practice:

Factorize: a) $x^2 + 12x + 20$ **b)** $d^2 - 7d - 30$
c) $a^2 + 3a - 10$ **d)** $8 + 2p - p^2$

Answers on page 308.

When there is no single power

If they throw this at you: $x^2 - 16$, then it's a special case called **the difference of two squares**.

You end up with one + bracket and one − bracket $(x + \quad)(x - \quad)$ with the same number in both. The number is the square root of the constant, so in this case it's 4. Let's test it and see: $(x + 4)(x - 4)$ $= x^2 + 4x - 4x - 16 = x^2 - 16$.

Here's a chewier example: $4x^2 - 11 = (2x + \sqrt{11})(2x - \sqrt{11})$. You can see that the square root of 4 is 2, so that goes in front of both the x's in the brackets. Afterwards comes the square root of 11, one of which is + and the other is −.

Good news: You will not be asked to factorize something like $x^2 + 9$, because the + in the middle puts this question into a completely different league! It involves things called imaginary numbers which − luckily − you don't need to know for GCSE.

Well, that's a relief!

H: Tougher quadratics

So far we've only dealt with expressions that have one x^2 and the constant always provides the factors we need. Now let's try something tasty:

$$6x^2 - 5x - 21$$

What you have to do is use the factors of the x^2 coefficient *and* the factors of the constant to produce two numbers which then add or subtract to make the x coefficient. (For the purposes of this explanation we'll call these two numbers "magic numbers".) In this case it means juggling round the factors of 6 and 21 to produce two magic numbers that will make 5. This takes practice!

Follow this through to see what's going on: 6 can be made by 6×1 or 2×3 and 21 can be made by 3×7 or 21×1.

We need to choose which pair of factors from both the 6 and 21 will do the job and because the constant sign is – we need two magic numbers with a *difference* of 5.

> **TOP TIP**
> Try using the factors that are closer together first.

The "closer" factors of 6 are 2×3 and the closer factors of 21 are 3×7. We try pairing them off and see what we get.

$$6 = 2 \quad \times \quad 3$$
$$21 = 3 \quad \times \quad 7$$

- We times the factor 2 from the 6 with the 3 from the 21 and get $2 \times 3 = 6$
- That leaves the 3 from the 6 and the 7 from the 21 which gives $3 \times 7 = 21$

The two numbers we have made have a difference of 15. That didn't work so we'll use the same factors and pair them the other way round.

$$6 = 2 \times 3$$

$$21 = 3 \times 7$$

- We put the factor 3 from the 6 with the 3 from the 21 and get $3 \times 3 = 9$
- That leaves the 2 from the 6 and the 7 from the 21 which gives $2 \times 7 = 14$

Now we've got 14 and 9 . . . and $14 - 9 = 5$. This is good news. It means we've found our magic numbers are 14 and 9, and it might help to rewrite the original expression out now: $6x^2 - 5x - 21 = 6x^2 - 14x + 9x - 21$.

You'll see we've substituted the $- 5x$ for $- 14x$ and $+ 9x$.

Now draw out the brackets, putting the x's in the right place and leaving gaps like this: $(x \quad)(x \quad)$.

First put in the factors of 6 that we're using. These are 3 and 2: $(3x \quad)(2x \quad)$. When we multiply these up it gives the $6x^2$ we want. So far so good.

The other two numbers to go in are the factors of 21 that we are using, which are 7 and 3. We must make sure we get them in the right place to produce the magic numbers. To make 14 the 7 must be multiplied by the 2 so the 7 goes in the other bracket from the 2: $(3x \quad 7)(2x \quad)$.

That means the 3 goes in the remaining place: $(3x \quad 7)(2x \quad 3)$ Finally we have to put the signs in. As the original expression had two $-$ signs, we need a $+$ and a $-$, but which way round do they go? As the x coefficient was $- 5$, we need to ensure that when we multiply these brackets out we get $- 14x$ and $+ 9x$. Therefore the − sign goes to the 7. The final answer is: $(3x − 7)(2x + 3)$

Phew! Test this by multiplying it out.

Here's one more example:

$$4x^2 − 35x + 24$$

First job, check the factors of 4 and 24: 4 can be 4×1 or 2×2, and 24 can be 24×1, 12×3, 8×3 or 6×4.

Oh dear − tons to choose from! Anyway as the constant sign is + we need to make two magic numbers that ADD to 35.

There's a slight clue here. 35 is an odd number, so avoid pairs of even factors, as they will only ever give you even numbers. That means we can avoid 2×2 and also 6×4. The factors of 4 we need must be the 4×1, and let's try the 8×3 from the 24 set. If we pair off $4 \times 8 = 32$ and $1 \times 3 = 3$ they add to give 35. Utter joy. . . $(4x \quad)(x \quad)$

We've already put in the 4 and the 1 (of course we don't actually need to write the 1), so what do we need to multiply the 4 by? Answer: 8 − so put that in the OTHER bracket from the 4, and put the 3 in the gap. . . And because we started with a − + expression we know both signs are −. $(4x − 3)(x − 8)$

If you expand it, you'll find it works.

One more:

$$15 − 7x − 4x^2$$

If there is a negative x^2 coefficient, then put the x's on the right hand side of the bracket: $(\quad x)(\quad x)$. Just fill in the gaps as normal. As both signs are − in the original expression, you know that there will be a + and − in the final brackets and that you need to use the factors of 15 and 4 to get two magic numbers with a *difference* of 7. Try it yourself. (Answer on page 308.)

By the way, if you are reading this book through page by page, you've just got past what many people would think was the hardest bit!

Whooopee!

If your head goes completely blank when trying to get the factors for quadratics, you might find the "quadratic formula" coming later will help you.

H: Simplifying algebra

If you get something really ugly like this:

$(3a + 1)(a^2 - 4ab) + (2a^2 + a)(2b - a)$

...then you can usually get rid of some of it.

The first thing to do is expand the brackets all out and get a load of simple terms.

That gives us: $3a(a^2 - 4ab) + (a^2 - 4ab) + 2a^2(2b - a) + a(2b - a)$, which becomes: $3a^3 - 12a^2b + a^2 - 4ab + 4a^2b - 2a^3 + 2ab - a^2$

Now shuffle it all around so that the like terms come next to each other: $3a^3 - 2a^3 - 12a^2b + 4a^2b + a^2 - a^2 - 4ab + 2ab$.

Next you can add or subtract the like terms: $a^3 - 8a^2b - 2ab$.

And you might even want to finish by factorizing. In this case we can divide everything by a and we get: $a(a^2 - 8ab - 2b)$.

H: Indices in algebra

Indices in algebra work just as you might expect:

$(a + 3)^3 = (a + 3)(a + 3)(a + 3)$

But be particularly aware of negative indices: $x^{-1} = \frac{1}{x}$ and $g^{-3} = \frac{1}{g^3}$, and it's the same if there are brackets: $(r-3)^{-2} = \frac{1}{(r-3)^2} = \frac{1}{(r-3)(r-3)}$

To multiply two terms, you just add the indices together: $s^3 \times s^4 = s^7$ and $q^5 \times q^{-3} = q^2$.

To divide two terms, subtract the indices: $\frac{c^4}{c} = c^4 \div c = c^3$ and $\frac{m^2}{m^6} = m^2 \div m^6 = m^{-4}$ and $\frac{g^7}{g^{-3}} = g^7 \div g^{-3} = g^{10}$.

TOP TIP

If two terms have different indices, you cannot add or subtract them. So if you have $d^3 + d^2$ or $a^5 - a^3$ there's absolutely nothing you can do with them. Best to swallow your disappointment and move on. . .

Formulae

(If you have more than one formula, they are supposed to be called "formulae" because the word comes from Latin.)

A typical question looks like this:

> **If $p = a(b - c)^2 + d$ find the value of p when $a = 6$, $b = 7$, $c = 5$ and $d = 4$.**

All you do is swap the letters for the numbers you are given. Here you get: $p = 6(7 - 5)^2 + 4$.

> Here's the important bit. You *must* do the sums in this order:
> **1.** Anything in brackets.
> **2.** Any powers.
> **3.** Any multiplying and dividing.
> **4.** Any adding and subtracting.

So, going through these four steps, we get: $p = 6(7 - 5)^2 + 4 = 6(2)^2 + 4 = 6 \times 4 + 4 = 24 + 4 = 28$.

Here's another:

> $x = 3\sqrt{2y - z}$. Find x if $y = 11$ and $z = 6$.

$x = 3\sqrt{2 \times 11 - 6} = 3\sqrt{22 - 6} = 3\sqrt{16} = 3 \times 4 = 12$. Note that the square root is a power, but anything inside the square root sign is treated as if it's in a bracket. That's why we sorted out the insides of the root sign first. If in doubt, always multiply and divide *before* you add or subtract.

Sometimes you need to adjust a formula before you can use it – this is explained later, after we've looked at equations.

Algebra equations: linear

There is something wonderful about doing algebra equations in exams – it's one of the very few times when you can check you've got your answers correct! If you're not sure of the German word for "pineapple" or you don't know how many sheep there are in New Zealand then you can't do much about it. But with algebra equations, you KNOW when you're right!

Equations that don't have any powers in them (such as squares or cubes) are called **linear equations**.

A very simple equation would be $a + 3 = 12$. It's like a little puzzle, and you have to work out what a equals, so you have to rearrange it so that a is by itself on one side of the equals sign. There is one massive rule for ALL equations from the simplest to the hardest:

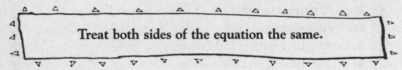

Treat both sides of the equation the same.

The left-hand side is usually abbreviated to LHS and right-hand side to RHS. Let's see how a few work:

$$a + 3 = 12$$

To solve it we want to get rid of the +3 from the LHS, so we subtract 3 from both sides and we get: $a + 3 - 3 = 12 - 3$ and this becomes $a = 9$. That's the answer! It's easy to check because you just go back to the original equation and put in 9 instead of a. You get $9 + 3 = 12$, which is correct.

$$5f = 35$$

We need to get rid of the 5 on the LHS. The 5 is multiplying, so we'll divide both sides by 5. We get $5f \div 5 = 35 \div 5$ so $f = 7$.

$$3g - 4 = 11$$

First we'll add 4 to both sides (to get rid of the − 4) and get $3g - 4 + 4 = 11 + 4$. If you want you can just write $3g$ instead of $3g - 4 + 4$ because the + 4 and − 4 cancel out, but you can write out the whole thing if it helps you. $3g = 15$, so if we divide both sides by 3 we get $3g ÷ 3 = 15 ÷ 3$ which gives $g = 5$. Again, you can write g straight away instead of $3g ÷ 3$ if you like, but write it in full if it helps.

> **"Changing the sign"**
> A lot of people talk about moving something across to the other side of an equation and changing the sign. In the first example the + 3 moved over to become − 3. In the second example the × 5 moved across and changed to ÷ 5. There's nothing wrong with this providing you understand why it works. It can get confusing when you are dividing by negative numbers, so if in any doubt remember to *treat both sides the same*.

Here's a typical equation to solve: $-4(p + 6) = 9 - p$

Always expand any brackets first: $-4p - 24 = 9 - p$

Get all the p's to the LHS by

  adding p to both sides: $-4p - 24 + p = 9 - p + p$

Simplify the terms: $-3p - 24 = 9$

Get all the numbers to the RHS

  by adding 24 to both sides: $-3p - 24 + 24 = 9 + 24$

Simplify the terms: $-3p = 33$

Divide both sides by − 3: $\frac{-3p}{-3} = \frac{33}{-3}$

So the answer is: $p = -11$

Now try these:

> **Solve the following equations:**
> **a)** $2x + 3 = 15$ **b)** $3y = 10 + y$ **c)** $6y + 1 = 9 - 2$
> **d)** $3(x+4) = 2(x+5)$

Answers on page 308.

F: Making your own equations

Sometimes a problem is written out and you have to make it into an equation that you can solve.

> **If you subtract 3 from a number then divide the answer by 2, you get the same as if you multiplied 2 by the number and then subtracted 12.**

Work this through bit by bit, converting the question to algebra. Let's call the number n.

"If you subtract 3 from a number" $n - 3$
"then divide the answer by 2" $(n - 3) \div 2$
"you get the same as" $=$
"if you multiplied 2 by n" $2n$
"and subtracted 12" $2n - 12$
So the equation is: $(n - 3) \div 2 = 2n - 12$

Of course when you do this you only have to write the final equation out. It's only been done in stages here so that you can see exactly what's going on. See if you can get the answer and then check by putting your answer into your original equation to make sure it works. (Answer on page 308.)

Three buskers have been out. Spud got twice as much as Dreggs who got 20p less than Ringo. Together they made £4.60. How much did each person make?

> **TOP TIP**
> When constructing equations, always make it clear what letters you are using.

Let s = Spud's money. So Dreggs got $\frac{s}{2}$ and Ringo got $\frac{s}{2}$ + 20. Put them all together and... $s + \frac{s}{2} + \frac{s}{2} + 20 = 460$. Go on, you finish it. (Answer on page 308.)

Here's one for you to try.

> **Divide £370 between John, Paul and Petunia so John has £20 more than Paul and Petunia has £30 more than John. How much does each person get?**

Answer on page 308.

Sometimes examiners make up a more complicated story for you to sort out. Try this one:

A group of explorers are trekking through the jungle. On the first day exactly one quarter of them die of food poisoning. On the second day, four fall off a rope bridge into the chasm. On day three half of the survivors are eaten by man-eating spiders. On day four a giant vulture carries off one more person. On day five the final six survivors reach their base camp. Make an equation and then solve it to find how many people started out. Check your answer with the story.

Answer on page 308.

TOP TIP
Always write your answer in full and remember the units.

H: Rearranging formulae

The volume of a sphere is given by the equation: $V = \frac{4}{3}\pi r^3$ If you've got the radius "r" then working out the volume should be no problem. But what if you know the volume and want the radius? At the moment "r" is buried inside this expression, but you need just "r" left by itself. It's a bit like dissecting a frog: you take away the outer bits and work your way in until you've got right to the middle. Just like any equation, you can do what you like so long as you **treat both sides the same**:

We start with: $\qquad\qquad\qquad\qquad V = \frac{4}{3}\pi r^3$

Multiply both sides by 3 to get: $\qquad 3V = 4\pi r^3$

Divide both sides by 2π: $\qquad\qquad \frac{3V}{4\pi} = r^3$

Take the cube root of both sides: $\qquad \left(\frac{3V}{4\pi}\right)^{\frac{1}{3}} = r$

Here's another formula: $p = \left(\frac{3-q}{4}\right)^{\frac{1}{2}}$, but we need to find q.

Square both sides: $\qquad\qquad\qquad\qquad p^2 = \frac{3-q}{4}$

Multiply by 4: $\qquad\qquad\qquad\qquad 4p^2 = 3 - q$

Subtract the 3 (and swap
the sides round): $\qquad\qquad\qquad -q = 4p^2 - 3$

As we'd rather have $+ q$,
multiply everything by -1: $\qquad q = 3 - 4p^2$

H: Adjusting trickier formulae

Sometimes the letter you want appears in the formula more than once, so it takes a bit more juggling round.

Make x the subject of $ab = xcy - 3xz$

Factorize RHS: $\qquad\qquad\qquad\qquad ab = x(cy - 3z)$

Swap sides and divide by the bracket: $\quad x = \frac{ab}{cy - 3z}$

That wasn't too bad but now let's undo this beauty...

Make v the subject of $A = \sqrt{v + 1} - 2$

Add 2 to both sides: $\qquad\qquad\quad A + 2 = \sqrt{v + 1}$

Square both sides: $\qquad\qquad\quad (A + 2)^2 = v + 1$

Expand bracket $\qquad\qquad\qquad A^2 + 4A + 4 = v + 1$

Subtract 1 from both sides: $\qquad A^2 + 4A + 4 - 1 = v$

Swap the sides round: $\qquad\qquad v = A^2 + 4A + 3$

Finish in style by factorizing: $\quad v = (A + 3)(A + 1)$

The secret is just to move the bits about and expand any brackets until you can separate the letter you need from everything else.

Now try one yourself.

Make y the subject $Q = 3y + a^2 y$

Answer on page 308.

Algebra equations: quadratic

I: We've already seen how to factorize quadratics like $x^2 - 6x - 16$. A quadratic equation is just the same but has $= 0$ at the end, so you might be asked to solve: $x^2 - 8x + 15 = 0$.

Before we go on you should know that there is something rather groovy about quadratic equations – nearly all of them have two answers! You'll be expected to find both.

Let's look at this equation: $x^2 - 6x - 16 = 0$. First factorize the quadratic expression. In a twinkling you'll get: $(x - 8)(x + 2)$.

For this equation to work, one or other of the two brackets must $= 0$. It doesn't matter which, but as long as one of them $= 0$ then when you multiply it by the other, you'll get 0 so the equation balances. That's how we get two possible answers: $(x - 8) = 0$ or $(x + 2) = 0$.

We have two pathetically simple equations here: If $x - 8 = 0$ then $x = 8$. Or if $x + 2 = 0$ then $x = -2$. So the solutions to the equation $x^2 - 6x - 16 = 0$ are that $x = 8$ or -2.

Of course we can test these values: If $x = 8$ then $x^2 - 6x - 16 = 64 - 48 - 16 = 0$ YES! If $x = -2$ then $x^2 - 6x - 16 = 4 + 12 - 16 = 0$ YES AGAIN!

That's how to solve quadratic equations *by factorizing*.

There's no short cuts here, you've GOT to practise, so. . .

Factorize and solve the following equations:
a) $x^2 - 3x + 2 = 0$ **b)** $x^2 - 4x - 5 = 0$ **c)** $x^2 - 5x - 14 = 0$
d) $4x^2 + 11x - 3 = 0$ **e)** $4x^2 + 8x - 21 = 0$

Answers on page 309.

Sadly you might be asked to solve quadratic equations that do NOT have nice factors, but in this case you might be told to use. . .

H: The quadratic formula

Not all quadratic equations factorize, but luckily some superbrain invented a method which will solve *any* quadratic equation. If you are asked to solve a quadratic equation to a number of decimal places, this is usually the way you are expected to do it.

There are two things you need to know. Here's the first:

$$x = \frac{-b \pm \sqrt{b^2 - 4ac}}{2a}$$

In words this means "x equals minus b plus or minus the square root of b squared minus four a times c all over two a." If the exam paper asks you to use the formula, they will write it out for you, but you should try and learn it anyway. Read it out aloud a few times and click your fingers to make it rappy. (In exams, if you see people trying to quietly click their fingers and mouth some words, you'll know what question they're on!)

Don't forget that the formula starts with *minus b*. It's a very common mistake which can make your life truly awful.

The second thing you have to know is a lot simpler:

$$ax^2 + bx + c = 0$$

Here's how you use the formula. Suppose you have to solve this: $4x^2 - 5x - 6 = 0$. It's the same as $ax^2 + bx + c$ but now you know: $a = 4$, $b = -5$ and $c = -6$. (Note: the minus signs are important!)

All you do is put the values for a, b and c into the formula. (Notice that when the "$-b$" is replaced by the value $b = -5$, it becomes $+5$.) Make sure you work out all the bits in the right order, so start inside the square root sign. You get:

$$x = \frac{-b \pm \sqrt{b^2 - 4ac}}{2a} = \frac{5 \pm \sqrt{25 - 4 \times 4 \times -6}}{2 \times 4}$$

$$= \frac{5 \pm \sqrt{25 + 96}}{8} = \frac{5 \pm \sqrt{121}}{8} = \frac{5 \pm 11}{8}$$

The "$\pm$" (plus or minus) sign gives the two solutions because we add 11 to get the first and subtract 11 to get the second.

1st solution: $x = (5 + 11) \div 8 = 16 \div 8 = 2$
2nd solution: $x = (5 - 11) \div 8 = -6 \div 8 = -0.75$

If you put these solutions into the original, they both work. Try it yourself.

You may well be asked to solve quadratic equations to a number of decimal places so let's see how an example works:

Solve $3x^2 + 7x - 2 = 0$ to three decimal places.

All you do is replace a, b and c by 3, 7 and -2 in the formula and get:

$$x = \frac{-7 \pm \sqrt{7^2 - 4 \times 3 \times -2}}{2 \times 3} = \frac{-7 \pm \sqrt{49 + 24}}{6}$$

$$= \frac{-7 \pm \sqrt{73}}{6}$$

Your calculator will tell you that $\sqrt{73}$ is 8·544 to three decimal places, so the two solutions are:

1st solution: $x = (-7 + 8 \cdot 544) \div 6 = 1 \cdot 544 \div 6 = 0 \cdot 257$
2nd solution: $x = (-7 - 8 \cdot 544) \div 6 = -15 \cdot 544 \div 6 = -2 \cdot 591$

Again you should check the answers. Go on, it's good practice. Finished? Good. Here's one for you to try:

> **A rectangle has sides of length $(2x - 3)$ and $(3x - 5)$ and the area is 5. Find two values for x.**

Answers on page 309.

Inequalities

What are inequalities?

I: These are equations that use the "less than" or "greater than" signs instead of "equals". Here are what the signs mean:

$x < 4$ x is less than 4
$x \leq 8$ x is less than or equal to 8
$x > 3$ x is greater than 3
$x \geq 0$ x is greater than or equal to 0

TOP TIP

The "wide" end of the arrow is always the bigger number and the "thin" end is the smaller number.

Equations that use these signs work in exactly the same way that "equals" equations work, though there are two things to be aware of:

- **If you swap the sides over you must also change the sign round.** Although $2 > 1$ is true, you can't just swap them over and say $1 > 2$. If you swap sides, you must change the sign round so $2 > 1$ becomes $1 < 2$.

- **If you divide through by a negative you must change the sign round.** If you have $-15 < -6$ you CAN divide through by $+3$ to give $-5 < -2$. However, if you divide through by -3 you must change the sign round to get $5 > 2$.

Let's see one in action:

$$3x + 5 < 4(x - 2)$$
$$3x + 5 - 5 < 4x - 8 - 5$$
$$3x < 4x - 13$$
$$3x - 4x < -13$$
$$-x < -13$$

And when you multiply through by -1 don't forget to change the sign round so that $x > 13$.

111

I: Ranges of values

Inequality signs are used to show a range of values. Suppose you set off to the shops with £10. How much money will you come back with? Let's call the amount left over L and we can say: £0 ≤ L ≤ £10. This is exactly the same as two inequalities: £0 ≤ L and L ≤ £10.

It tells us that you could have all £10 left if you don't spend anything, or you might have nothing left if you spend the lot, or you might have some amount between the two.

I: Inequalities on the number line

You may even be asked to mark a range of values on a number line, for example:

> There's a parent/toddler group meeting in the local scout hut. The toddlers are aged between 1 and 3 and the parents are aged between 18 and 28. Write these values as inequalities. Mark them on a number line representing their ages.

Easy! If the toddlers' ages = T then 1 ≤ T ≤ 3. If the parents' ages = P then 18 ≤ P ≤ 28.

```
     T                                    P
  0  2  4  6  8 10 12 14 16 18 20 22 24 26 28 30
```

age in years

112

Graphs

There are two things to know about graphs:

- Graphs are a convenient way of showing how two things are linked. Some describe real situations, and others can help solve algebra problems!
- Graphs are absolutely 100% certain to turn up. If you're sitting a maths exam but don't see any mention of graphs then YOU ARE IN THE WRONG EXAM. Hurl yourself head first through the door immediately.

F: Real situation graphs

If you have a job, you could use a graph to show how much money you get for any amount of hours that you work.

This graph shows the rewards for pearl diving in Grimsby for which you get paid £6 per hour. You'll see there are two "axes".

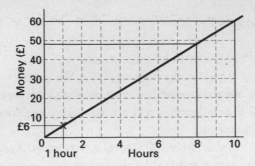

The one along the bottom (the "horizontal axis") is marked in hours and the one up the side (the "vertical axis") is marked with money in pounds.

> **TOP TIP**
> Always label the axes of your graph.

To draw this graph, you fill in one or two details you know. The obvious one is that if you work for 0 hours then you get 0 money, so you can put a cross in the corner where both axes read "0". For 1 hour you get £6, so you mark a point directly above the 1 hour mark, and directly along from £6. You could also make a few other marks – an easy one is if you work 10 hours you'd get 10 × £6 which is £60, so you put a mark at the appropriate place. You then join these marks up.

Suppose you worked for 8 hours. To find your wages you just find the point on the line directly above the 8 hour mark. If you look over to the side, you'll see this mark is directly along from the £48 position – so that would be your wages. The good thing is that if you worked for e.g. $5\frac{1}{2}$ hours, the graph quickly tells you what you've made without you having to multiply $6 \times 5\frac{1}{2}$.

TOP TIP
Time usually goes on the horizontal axis. We could have put money along the bottom and time up the side if we really wanted, but it would be unusual and could lead to confusion.

Help! Time on the vertical axis. What's going on?

I: Gradients
If a road goes up a hill, the steepness is described as the gradient. This can be accurately described in numbers as a fraction which is calculated like this:

$$\text{Gradient} = \frac{\text{How far you go upwards}}{\text{How far you go along}}$$

So if you go along 100 m and rise up 10 m, then the gradient is $\frac{10}{100}$ which is $\frac{1}{10}$ or 10%. In case you have trouble remembering which way round the fraction should be:

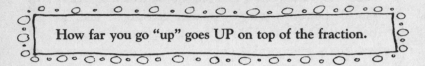

How far you go "up" goes UP on top of the fraction.

Lines on graphs also have gradients, and they are calculated in exactly the same way. For the wages graph, if you go "along" one hour then you go "up" £6. This means the gradient is $\frac{£6}{1\,hour}$, which is the same as saying £6 per hour.

Let's look at another graph now:

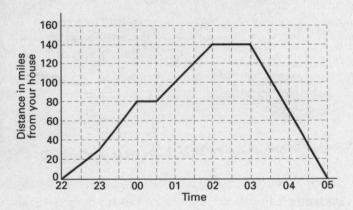

You're guest DJ at a club 140 miles away and this graph describes the journey there and back.

- In the hour between 22:00 and 23:00 the line on the graph went up 30 miles, so the gradient shows your speed as 30 miles per hour.
- By midnight the total distance is 80 miles, so you did 50 miles between 23:00 and 00:00. The speed for the second hour was

50 miles per hour. Note that the line on the graph is steeper which shows the increased speed.

- Between 00:00 and 00:30 the line is horizontal. If you go no distance in half an hour – obviously you're not moving! So this line indicates that you were taking a break.
- Between 00:30 and 2:00 the line rises a further 60 miles. The gradient in miles per hour is therefore $\frac{60}{1.5}$, which works out at 40 miles per hour.
- You stayed 140 miles away between 2:00 and 3:00 – because you were at the club being loud and groovy.

- Finally, between 3:00 and 5:00 the line comes *down* 140 miles. Because the line slopes downwards, this is a negative gradient so your speed is − 70mph. The minus sign shows you are *reducing* the distance from your house. If you want to travel at negative speed, then you have two choices: drive in reverse or turn the car round. The second choice is recommended.

There are more details on how gradients show speed and acceleration coming up on page 141.

F: Recognizing patterns on graphs

Here's a festive graph. Christmas cards are 80p for a packet of 5, so how many can you afford?

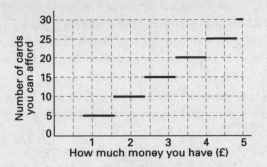

You'll see the line "jumps". For instance, if you have £2.39 then you can only afford two packets which makes 10 cards. However, if you find another 1p in your old anorak hood then suddenly you can afford 15 cards.

Suppose you have a straight-sided vase that you're filling with water.

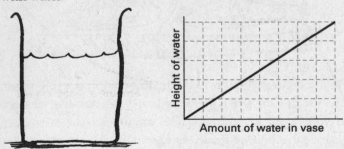

You could plot how much water you need to put in to get the level up. Because the sides are straight, if you put in twice as much water, then the level will be twice as high.

This odd vase gives a different graph!

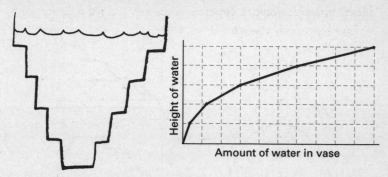

It doesn't take much water to fill the bottom section, so the line rises steeply on the graph. For the second section it takes rather more water to fill it, so the line is not so steep. By the time it comes to filling the top big section it takes lots of water, so the line is almost horizontal.

Filling this vase would give a nice curved line on the graph:

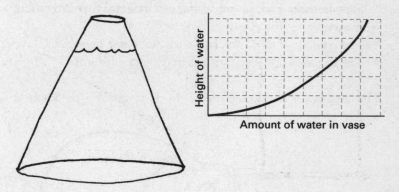

You'll see that to start with you need a lot of water to raise the height a bit, but as the level gets nearer to the top then a small amount makes a bigger difference.

You need to be able to picture how two things vary with each other, so have a look at these:

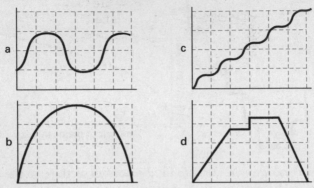

Each of the graphs represents one of the following:

- The height of a ball being thrown in the air.
- The depth of water in a basin which is slowly filled up. (After a few minutes a large stone is dropped in it and then after a few more minutes the plug is pulled out.)
- The amount of air in an elephant's lungs as it breathes.
- The distance travelled by a bus making regular stops.

The graphs all have time along the bottom. Which graph is which? (Answers on page 309.)

Graphs and algebra

How are they linked?

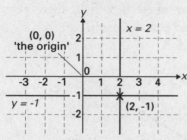

I: One of the strangest yet most satisfying bits of maths is that you can use graphs to solve algebra equations. The first thing you need to do is draw two axes. The horizontal axis is called the "x" axis and the vertical axis is the "y" axis. The axes meet at the point where $x = 0$ and $y = 0$ and this is called the **origin**. Any point on this graph can be described by giving values for x and y.

The vertical line cuts the x axis at 2, so this line represents $x = 2$. The horizontal line cuts the y axis at -1, so this represents $y = -1$. The point where the two lines meet is described as $(2, -1)$.

TOP TIP

The x value always comes first: remember that x comes before y in the alphabet. Another way of remembering it is to think of an aeroplane taking off: it goes along before it goes up – or down!

Before you draw axes, there are a few things you need to decide:

- The maximum and minimum values of x you will need.
- The maximum and minimum values of y you will need.

A very simple example is: $y = 3x$ for $0 \leq x \leq 10$. This means that we want to know what value y has for any value of x between 0 and 10.

What is the maximum value of y? If $x = 10$, then $y = 30$. What is the minimum value of y? If $x = 0$, then $y = 0$. We can then draw our axes and plot the graph.

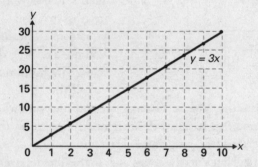

Notice that it doesn't matter if the numbers on the y axis are closer together than the numbers on the x axis.

Although this graph is extremely simple, if you weren't sure where the line goes you would start by filling out a little table:

$x =$		0	1	2	3	4	5	6	7	8	9	10
$y = 3x =$		0	3	6	... and so on.							

All you do is fill in the y values on the table and in this case each one will be 3 times the x value because our equation is $y = 3x$.

When you have all the y values you mark them on the graph and then join them up with a line.

TOP TIPS
Mark the points with crosses, not dots. Make sure your pencil is sharp (without being lethal) and your eraser is clean.

ha ha

Whenever you draw a line on a graph, write in the equation somewhere close to it.

You can find the gradient of the line by looking at any little section of it.

$$\text{The gradient is: } \frac{\text{the difference in } y}{\text{the difference in } x}$$

If you look at the bit between $x = 6$ and $x = 7$ on the graph on page 122, the difference in x is 1. The y value goes up from $y = 18$ to $y = 21$ so the difference in y is 3. If you like: the line has "gone along" 1 and "gone up" 3. This makes the gradient $\frac{3}{1}$ which is just 3.

Let's have another equation: $y = 3x + 2$ for $-5 \leq x \leq +5$.

Max value of y is when $x = +5$, so max $y = 3 \times 5 + 2 = 17$. Min value of y is when $x = -5$, so min $y = 3 \times (-5) + 2 = -15 + 2 = -13$.

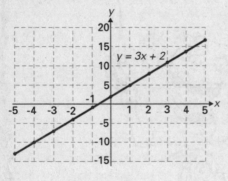

You'll see on the graph that the x and y axes now cross to allow room for the negative numbers.

If you wanted to make a table for the graph, you need to show a bit more detail. First there's a line of "$3x$" and then another line for "$+ 2$". Once you've filled in all these values (it doesn't take long) you go along and add each column up together to give each value of y.

$x =$	-5	-4	-3	-2	-1	0	1	2	3	4	5
$3x =$	-15	-12	-9	-6	-3	0	3	6	9	12	15
$+2 =$	$+2$	$+2$	$+2$	$+2$	$+2$	$+2$	$+2$	$+2$	$+2$	$+2$	$+2$
$y = 3x + 2 =$	-13	-10	-7	-4	-1	2	5	8	11	14	17

If you compare the last two graphs you'll see that they both have a gradient of 3. In other words the "+ 2" in the second equation did not affect the gradient, instead all it did was move the line so that it crosses the y axis at the value $y = + 2$. This is called the y **intercept**. Let's look at the equation again:

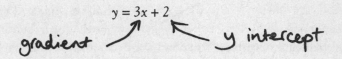

$$y = 3x + 2$$

gradient ↗   ↖ y intercept

These details work for ANY simple linear equation. If your equation is $y = mx + c$, for instance, then m = gradient and c = the y intercept.

I: Drawing linear graphs without a table

As long as the equation only has single powers of x and y, then the line on the graph will ALWAYS be straight. Better still, you don't actually need to draw out the table of values.

Suppose you've got $2y + x = -4$. The first thing we need to do is just get y by itself, so subtract x from both sides, and then divide everything by 2: $y = \frac{-x-4}{2} = \frac{-x}{2} - 2$

If you compare this to $y = mx + c$ then you can see $m = -\frac{1}{2}$ and $c = -2$ This tells us that the line has a gradient of $-\frac{1}{2}$ and it crosses the y axis at $y = -2$. Drawing the graph is easy.

TOP TIP
If you are not told the range of values for x, use $-5 \leq x \leq +5$.

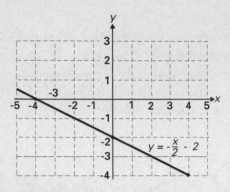

Put a little mark on the y axis at the (0, – 2) place. As the gradient is – $\frac{1}{2}$ move along from the mark 1 place and move *down* half a place. (You move down because the gradient is negative). You now have two marks on your graph, so all you do is draw a straight line that goes through them both. However. . .

TOP TIP

As an extra check, always work out a third value for x and y. Choose any value for x you like: in this case we'll have x = 4. When we put this into $y = -\frac{x}{2} - 2$ we find that y = – 4. This extra mark should be in line with the other two; if not then you've gone wrong somewhere!

Simultaneous equations

I: Before we go on with graphs, we're just going to catch up on a bit more algebra. We've already seen equations with one unknown number, but sometimes you are asked to solve equations with *two unknowns*. The only way you can do this is to have two equations which you solve *simultaneously*. To get your head round all this, it's best to label the equations A and B. Let's see an example:

A) $2p = 3q + 4$ B) $p - 2q = 1$

There are two methods you can use, and with a bit of practice you'll realize when to use which.

Method 1: Substitution

What you do here is adjust one of the equations so that it just has one of the letters by itself on the left. If we take equation B we can add $2q$ to each side and get: $p = 1 + 2q$.

This is super because now we can substitute $(1 + 2q)$ for p in equation A. $2(1 + 2q) = 3q + 4$. Now we can work this out: $2 + 4q = 3q + 4$, so $4q - 3q = 4 - 2$, so $q = 2$.

We've got a value for q, so now we rush back excitedly to the re-arranged version of equation B, but we replace q with 2: $p = 1 + 2 \times 2 = 1 + 4 = 5$. Done it! The answers are $p = 5$ and $q = 2$. You can check this by trying these values in equation A.

Method 2: Elimination

First re-arrange your equations if necessary so that all the letters are on the LHS: A) $2p - 3q = 4$ B) $p - 2q = 1$

What we need to do is multiply one (or both if necessary) equations so that one of the letters has the same coefficient in both A and B. This sounds tricky, but watch:

Multiply both sides of B by 2:	$2p - 4q = 2$
Now we have $2p$ in both equations.	
Write A underneath:	$2p - 3q = 4$
Subtract equation A from B × 2:	$2p - 2p - 4q + 3q = 2 - 4$
	$-q = -2$ so q = 2

(If you're not happy about subtracting equations, look at it in two parts. First we subtract the LHS of A from the LHS of B × 2, so it's $(2p - 4q) - (2p - 3q)$. Expand the brackets to get $2p - 4q - 2p + 3q$, then simplify to get $-q$ on the LHS. Then subtract the RHS of A from the RHS of B × 2 which is just 2 − 4 leaving − 2 on the RHS.)

Once you've got $q = 2$, you can put into either of the equations to find p.

Here's a tougher one which we'll try both ways:

   A) $3s + 2r = 5$ **B)** $3r − 4s = 33$

Substitution:

If you're not sure where to start, see which letter has the lowest coefficient. In this case it's the $2r$ in equation A so we'll use A to get an expression for r. $3s + 2r = 5$, becomes $2r = 5 − 3s$, so $r = \frac{5 - 3s}{2}$.

Put this into B and get:	$3\frac{(5 - 3s)}{2} − 4s = 33$
Multiply through by 2:	$3(5 − 3s) − 8s = 66$
Expand bracket:	$15 − 9s − 8s = 66$
Simplify:	$− 17s = 66 − 15 = 51$
And we get:	$s = − 3$

Put this value into A and get : $3(−3) + 2r = 5$

                                       $− 9 + 2r = 5$

                                       $2r = 5 + 9 = 14$ so $r = 7$

You can check that $s = − 3$ and $r = 7$ by putting them into B.

Elimination:

As r has the lower coefficients in the two equations, that's the one we'll try to get rid of. We want r to have the same coefficients in both equations. The trick is to multiply equation A by the r coefficient in B (which is 3), and then multiply equation B by the r coefficient in A (which is 2).

Multiply A × 3 $\qquad$ $9s + 6r = 15$
Multiply B × 2 $\qquad$ $6r - 8s = 66$
Subtract B × 2 from A × 3 $\qquad$ $9s + 8s = -51$ and $s = -3$

And again, once you've got one result you can substitute it in either equation to get the other value.

I: Solving simultaneous equations with graphs

$\quad$ **A) $2y + x = 5$** $\qquad\qquad$ **B) $3y - 4x = 13$**

The first thing to do is convert each equation into the form $y = mx + c$. A) $y = \frac{5-x}{2} = \frac{-x}{2} + \frac{5}{2}$ B) $y = \frac{13+4x}{3} = \frac{4x}{3} + \frac{13}{3}$

These are both nice linear equations so they will produce two straight lines. You can make a little table for both, choosing 3 values for x in each.

Equation A

$x =$	0	1	2
$-\frac{x}{2} =$	0	-0.5	-1
$+\frac{5}{2} =$	$+2.5$	$+2.5$	$+2.5$
$y = -\frac{x}{2} + \frac{5}{2} =$	2.5	2	1.5

Equation B

$x =$	0	1	2
$\frac{4x}{3} =$	0	1.33	2.67
$+\frac{13}{3} =$	$+4.33$	$+4.33$	$+4.33$
$y = \frac{4x}{3} + \frac{13}{3} =$	4.33	5.67	7

When you draw the graph, allow quite a bit of space either side of the values that appear on your tables. Here we'll use $-5 \leq x \leq +5$ and $0 \leq y \leq 10$.

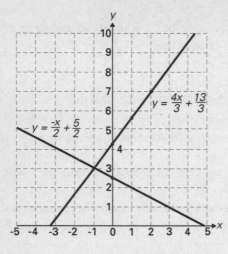

The good bit is that the place where the lines cross gives you the answer to the simultaneous equations. Here you can see the intersection is at $(-1, 3)$. Because this point is on both lines, the x and y values satisify both equations. Of course there's no harm in checking by putting these values in and seeing if they work!

Let's try equation A with $x = -1$ and $y = 3$. $2y + x = 5$ becomes $2 \times 3 + (-1) = 5$ which is $6 - 1 = 5$. It works!

Sometimes you end up using letters that are different to x and y. It's no problem though. . .

Desperate Dave bought gorgeous Glenda 3 boxes of chocolates and 2 bunches of flowers and spent £14.20. Hopeless Humphrey spent £15.50 on buying Glenda 5 of the same boxes of chocolates and one identical bunch of flowers. Glenda didn't go out with either of them, though. She was too busy working out how much each box of chocolates and each bunch of flowers cost. What should her answers be?

Let's call the cost of a box of chocs "*c*" and a bunch of flowers "*f*". If we put all the money into pence, the two equations are:

A) $3c + 2f = 1420$ B) $5c + f = 1550$

As the *f* coefficients are more friendly, we'll make both our equations into "*f* equals":

A) $f = \frac{1420}{2} - \frac{3c}{2} = 710 - \frac{3c}{2}$ B) $f = 1550 - 5c$

When we come to plot this, *f* will be on what is usually the *y* axis, and *c* will be on the *x* axis.

How long do the axes need to be?

As we know that neither item can cost a negative amount of money, we needn't bother with any negative axes. Also, if you look at equation B, it tells us that when $c = 0$ then $f = 1550$, so that must be the maximum value of *f*. Therefore the *f* axis goes up to 1550. Equation B also shows us that when $f = 0$ then *c* is 1550 ÷ 5 = 310, so that's the maximum *c* value.

Try drawing out some tables yourself and plotting these two lines. See where they intersect then check your answers in the equations. (Answers on page 309.)

TOP TIP
Draw your graph as large as you can. The ones in this book are only small to save space.

Non-linear graphs

If you are given an equation with any power of x that isn't 1, then the line on the graph will be curved. You need to recognize the distinctive patterns that equations including such things as x^2, x^3, $x^{\frac{1}{2}}$ or even $\frac{1}{x}$ include.

F: Drawing quadratic graphs

As you know, quadratic equations include x^2 and so quadratic graphs have x^2 in the equations. Surprise, surprise.

The simplest example is $y = x^2$ which makes an even "u" shape called a **parabola**. To plot this accurately you should make a table. Unlike linear graphs you need more than two or three points!

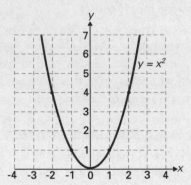

$x =$	-2	-1	-0.5	0	0.5	1	2
$y = x^2 =$	4	1	0.25	0	0.25	1	4

You'll notice the table includes $x = -0.5$ and $+0.5$ because plotting these extra two points helps you draw the "sharp" end of the curve more accurately. Also there are no negative values for y, so we don't need the y axis to extend below $y = 0$.

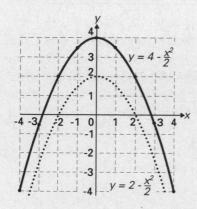

This graph shows two lines:

- $y = 4 - \frac{x^2}{2}$ is the solid line.
- $y = 2 - \frac{x^2}{2}$ is the dotted line.

Compare the $y = 4 - \frac{x^2}{2}$ line with the graph for $y = x^2$ and notice why the differences occur:

- The curve is upside down like an "n" shape. This is because the x^2 has a *negative* coefficient.
- The curve is not as "sharp" because the x^2 coefficient is a fraction.
- The y intercept is at $y = +4$. This is because the constant "4" appears in the equation.

Now look at the $y = 2 - \frac{x^2}{2}$ line. It's exactly the same as the $y = 4 - \frac{x^2}{2}$, but it crosses the y axis at $y = 2$. This shows that the only difference the constant makes is to move the position of the line up or down. To put it another way: *the constant does not change the shape of the line*.

Here's a more interesting equation: $y = 3x^2 - 4x - 7$.

If you think it looks a lot more complicated, don't be put off. If you need to draw a graph like this, do a table first:

$x =$	-3	-2	-1	0	1	2	3	4
$3x^2 =$	27	12	3	0	3	12	27	48
$-4x =$	$+12$	$+8$	$+4$	0	-4	-8	-12	-16
$-7 =$	-7	-7	-7	-7	-7	-7	-7	-7
$y = 3x^2 - 4x - 7 =$	32	13		0	-7	-8	-3	8	25

Now you just plot the points and here's what it looks like:

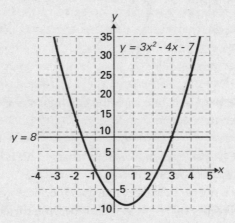

- The curve is a "u" shape because the x^2 coefficient is positive.
- If the y axis had been drawn to the same scale as the x axis, you would see that the curve is a lot more "pointed" than the $y = x^2$ graph. This is because the x^2 coefficient is 3.
- The y intercept is at $y = -7$ because -7 is the constant in the equation.
- The bottom of the curve has moved to the right. This is because of the "x" term in the equation.

I: Solving quadratic equations with graphs

If you had to solve the equation $3x^2 - 4x - 7 = 0$ you can read the answer straight off the graph! Remember there are two answers because it is a quadratic.

The line on the graph shows $y = 3x^2 - 4x - 7$, so we want to know what values x has when $y = 0$. Any point on the x axis is represented by $y = 0$, so look to see where the line crosses the x axis. The two places (as near as you can tell) are $x = -1$ and $x = 2\cdot3$.

Just to see if this works we'll quickly solve this with factorization and check the answer: $3x^2 - 4x - 7 = (3x - 7)(x + 1)$ so $x = -1$ or $+\frac{7}{3}$ which is $2\cdot33$.

The -1 solution was spot on, and $2\cdot3$ was very close! Obviously the better your drawing, then the closer you can get to the exact answers.

How about solving this equation: $3x^2 - 4x - 15 = 0$

Amazingly we can use the same graph. All we do is convert the LHS of this equation to the equation for the line we've drawn. If we add 8 to both sides we get: $3x^2 - 4x - 7 = 8$ Now we draw a line representing $y = 8$ and see where the curved line crosses it. We get answers of $x = -1\cdot6$ and $+3$.

H: Simultaneous quadratic equations on graphs

Wow! In terms of maths questions this is the giant cooked breakfast with extra toast and coffee. Tons of stuff is all lumped together into one question and splashed on to a graph, but if you just take it bit by bit there's a lot of marks to be gained here.

These are just the same as normal simultaneous equations – you just put two lines on your graph and see where they cross.

Take $\frac{x^2}{2} + x - \frac{1}{2} = 0$. All you do is shuffle it round so that the $\frac{x^2}{2}$ term is on its own: $\frac{x^2}{2} = \frac{1}{2} - x$.

Now you make two equations using each side: $y = \frac{x^2}{2}$ and $y = \frac{1}{2} - x$. Draw them out. . .

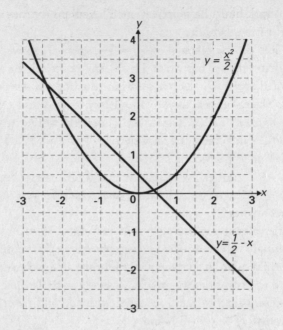

. . . and where the line cuts the curve, those are the two solutions.

The interesting thing is that if you draw a curve such as $y = \frac{x^2}{2}$ you can solve ANY quadratic equation that includes x^2. Suppose the question asks you to use the same graph to solve $x^2 - 3x + 1 = 0$ you would divide by 2 to get an $\frac{x^2}{2}$ term: $\frac{x^2}{2} - \frac{3x}{2} + \frac{1}{2} = 0$. You then get the $\frac{x^2}{2}$ on its own: $\frac{x^2}{2} = \frac{3x}{2} - \frac{1}{2}$. You've already plotted $y = \frac{x^2}{2}$ so all you do is draw in $y = \frac{3x}{2} - \frac{1}{2}$ and once again you've got two solutions.

By the way, cubic graphs come up occasionally. (These involve an x^3 term.) You can treat them in a similar way to quadratic graphs – just be aware that a quad graph only has one curve so it looks like a letter "u" or "n", but a cubic graph has a double curve, so it will look like a flattened letter "S". Very pretty they are too.

$y = x^3 + 2x^2 - x - 2$

Oh! What a gorgeous graph!

Other things about graphs

Here are a few more details you should be aware of:

I: The $\frac{1}{x}$ or reciprocal graph

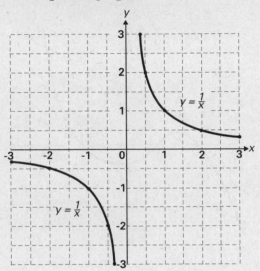

This is rather quaint because the equation $y = \frac{1}{x}$ actually produces two separate curves. As x gets closer to zero, y starts zooming off to infinity. When x drops just below the zero, y switches from + infinity to − infinity.

I: Parallel and perpendicular lines on graphs

We've already seen that if you have a linear equation such as $y = mx + c$ then m is the gradient. If two lines have the same gradient then they will be parallel, in other words they go for ever without touching.

If you have two lines with equations $y = mx + c$ and $y = nx + d$, the two gradients are m and n. If $m \times n = -1$ then the two lines will be perpendicular to each other, so they will cross at a right angle.

Let's see how all this looks:

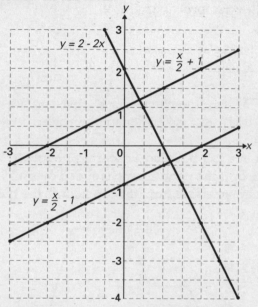

Here we've got: $y = \frac{x}{2} + 1$; $y = \frac{x}{2} - 1$ and $y = 2 - 2x$.

You'll see that the two lines with gradients of $\frac{1}{2}$ are parallel. The third line has a gradient of -2 and it intersects the other two lines at a right angle. If you multiply the different gradients together you get $\frac{1}{2} \times (-2) = -1$.

I: How the area of a speed/time graph shows distance

To see how this works we'll start with a very simple example:

A car travels for three hours at 40 mph. How far does it go?

We know that: Distance = Speed × Time so if you look at the graph the distance is represented by the shaded area. The area measures 40 mph up the side and 3 hours along the bottom so the area = 40 × 3 = 120 miles.

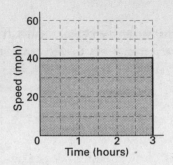

The area on *any* speed/time graph represents the distance travelled, so let's see a more interesting example.

A lift in a tall building is scaring people to bits. The graph over the page shows its speed over a 10-second journey as it goes from the top floor to the basement.

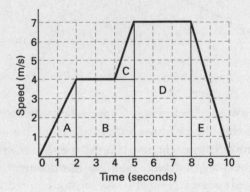

The speed "S" in metres per second (m/s or ms⁻¹) is shown plotted against the time "T" in seconds.

The total distance travelled by the lift is represented by the total area under the graph. Fortunately we can divide that into right-angled triangles and rectangles, as you can see from the picture, so we can work out the total area by working out the area of all the pieces and adding them together. The area of a triangle is half the base times the height. Area of A = $\frac{1}{2} \times 2 \times 4 = 4$. Area of B = $4 \times 3 = 12$. Area of C = $\frac{1}{2} \times 1 \times 3 = 1\cdot5$. Area of D = $3 \times 7 = 21$. Area of E = $\frac{1}{2} \times 2 \times 7 = 7$. So the total area = $4 + 12 + 1\cdot5 + 21 + 7 = 45\cdot5$ metres. Therefore the total distance travelled by the lift is $45\cdot5$ metres.

H: How speed/time graphs show acceleration

The graph is now going to tell us why the lift in the last example is so scary.

In the first two seconds the speed changes from 0 ms^{-1} to 4 ms^{-1}. Because it's getting faster, this is a **positive acceleration**.

$$\text{Acceleration} = \frac{\text{Change in speed}}{\text{Time}}$$

= the gradient of this piece of the graph.

Because the change in speed is 4 ms^{-1} and the time for it to change in is 2 seconds, the initial acceleration = $\frac{4}{2}$ = 2 ms^{-2} (or 2 metres per second per second). So for the first two seconds, people in the lift feel it speeding up.

You'll notice that between $t = 2$ and $t = 4$ the speed does not change, it just goes at a steady 4 ms^{-1}. But then between $t = 4$ and $t = 5$ the speed goes up to 7 ms^{-1}. This means that in one second it has increased by 3 ms^{-1}. (Acceleration = $\frac{3}{1}$ = 3 ms^{-2}.)

The graph shows us that suddenly the lift has speeded up again. It could cause anybody inside it to think the cable had snapped. Scary or what?

The graph shows the lift then continues for 3 seconds at 7 ms^{-1} but then the line slopes back down to zero. This is a negative gradient which indicates a negative acceleration (i.e. the lift is slowing down) from 7 to 0 in the last 2 seconds. (Acceleration = $-\frac{7}{2} = -3\frac{1}{2}$ ms^{-2}.)

If you were in the lift, this would almost feel like you'd hit the foundations. If you weren't scared before, you would be now!

H: Areas under curves: the trapezium method

If you're going for the higher level you may be asked to find the area under a curve using the "trapezium" method. Here's a rather heavy looking question. . .

> Draw the curve represented by the equation: $y = 6x - \frac{x^2}{2}$ for values $0 \leq x \leq 12$. Mark the area between $2 \leq x \leq 10$. Mark in strips of width 2 units, then use the trapezium method to calculate this area.

Phew! It's enough to have you chucking your desk out of the window, isn't it? Actually that would be a mistake because this sort of thing should be good for a few marks. Sometimes the graph will be drawn out for you with the strips already marked but in this case it isn't. Never mind, because if you have to do your own drawing it'll be worth some points by itself:

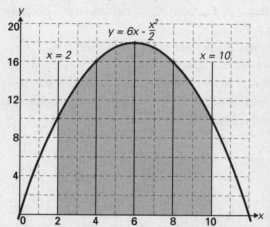

There! As well as the $y = 6x - \frac{x^2}{2}$ line, the lines $x = 2$ and $x = 10$ are also marked in and the area is shaded. Next you divide the area into strips. Here it's done with lines that represent $x = 4, 6$ and 8 because the question told you to mark strips of width 2 units.

And now the final detail. . .

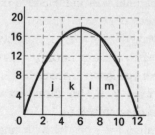

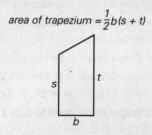

area of trapezium $= \frac{1}{2}b(s + t)$

Join the tops of the dividing lines up with slanting lines to make four trapeziums. (You can do this on your original graph. It's just

143

shown separately here for clarity.) Here the trapeziums are labelled j, k, l and m. The idea is to work out the area of each trapezium then add them together.

To get the area of one trapezium, you add together the parallel sides, times it by the base and divide by two. This is shown in the diagram as $\frac{1}{2}b(s + t)$.

The parallel sides are made with the dividing lines, so you're going to need to know the value for y for each of the values of x. But the good news about having plotted the graph is that you'll have already made a table that gives you them. Otherwise you could read them off the graph.

$x =$	2	4	6	8	10
$6x =$	12	24	36	48	60
$-\frac{x^2}{2} =$	-2	-8	-18	-32	-50
$y = 6x - \frac{x^2}{2} =$	10	16	18	16	10

For convenience, we'll introduce a bit more algebra code here. Instead of talking about "the value of y when x =1" we'll just say "y_1". Looking at the graph you can see that $y_2 = 10$, $y_4 = 16$, $y_6 = 18$ and so on.

If you look at trapezium j, the parallel sides are y_2 and y_4. Using the formula, we can see that the area of $j = \frac{1}{2} \times b(y_2 + y_4)$.

In the same way: $k = \frac{1}{2} \times b(y_4 + y_6)$, $l = \frac{1}{2} \times b(y_6 + y_8)$ and $m = \frac{1}{2} \times b(y_8 + y_{10})$.

If you add all four areas together you get:

Area $= \frac{1}{2} \times b(y_2 + 2y_4 + 2y_6 + 2y_8 + y_{10})$. This formula is worth recognizing! We'll look at it again in a minute.

To get the area we take the values for y off the table and put them in. (Also, as the base of each trapezium is 2, we make $b = 2$.)
Area $= \frac{1}{2} \times 2 (10 + 32 + 36 + 32 + 10) = 120$

144

Well, I feel a *bit* less like chucking my desk out the window.

Be aware that the trapezium method only gives an approximate value for the area, because we substituted small straight lines for the curve. They might ask you if the value you've worked out is too high or too low. In this case you'll see the value is a tiny bit low because the curve bulges outside the slanted lines at the top.

Let's just see how the trapezium formula arises with another example:

> **Find the area between $y = x^2 - 4x$ and $y = 0$ for $0 \leq x \leq 3$ using strips of width $\frac{1}{2}$.**

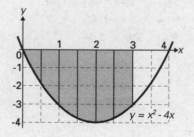

Here's what the graph looks like. (Notice that $y = 0$ is a way of saying "the x axis".)

You need values of y_0, $y_{0.5}$, y_1 ... up to y_3.

The width of the strips is the same as the base of each trapezium, so the formula will be: Area $= \frac{1}{2} \times \frac{1}{2}(y_0 + 2y_{0.5} + 2y_1 + 2y_{1.5} + 2y_2 + 2y_{2.5} + y_3)$

Notice that the brackets include two of each "y" value, except for the ones that come at either end. Also, the shape inside the curve between $x = 0$ and $x = 0{\cdot}5$ isn't a trapezium, it's actually a triangle. The formula allows for this automatically because $y_0 = 0$.

For a bit of practice, find the different values of y from the graph or from a table and use the formula to calculate this area. What do you get? (Answer on page 309.)

Here's another example:

> **An enormous ship takes 1 hour to come to a halt. As it slows, its speed is given by the equation $S = 20 - 30t + 10t^2$ where t is the time in hours and S is the speed in mph. How far does it travel before it stops?**

This graph is going to need a table plotting S against t and we know that $0 \le t \le 1$. We'll use values of t that differ by 0.2. (For a question like this, you will usually be told what values of t you need to plot.)

$t =$	0	0.2	0.4	0.6	0.8	1
$+ 20 =$	20	20	20	20	20	20
$- 30t =$	0	$- 6$	$- 12$	$- 18$	$- 24$	$- 30$
$+ 10t^2 =$	0	$+ 0.4$	$+ 1.6$	$+ 3.6$	$+ 6.4$	$+ 10$
$S = 20 - 30t + 10t^2 =$	20	14.4	9.6	5.6	2.4	0

We can make a trapezium formula that says: Distance = Area under curve = $\frac{1}{2} \times 0.2(S_0 + 2S_{0.2} + 2S_{0.4} + 2S_{0.6} + 2S_{0.8} + S_1)$. (Here $S_{0.2}$ means "the value of S when $t = 0.2$".)

You can finish this now: take the values off the table and work out the answer. Remember that this will only be an approximate answer – so look at the graph and decide if it will be higher or lower than the exact answer. (Answer on page 309.)

H: Constructing gradients to find acceleration

We've seen that the gradient of a speed/time graph shows acceleration. If you look at the graph of the big ship slowing down you could draw tangents to answer questions like "What is the ship's acceleration after 0.2 hours?" or "What is the ship's acceleration after 0.8 hours?"

You might like to draw this graph out yourself using the information supplied and then draw tangents to see what answers you get. Note: as the speed is in miles per hour and the time is in hours, when you work out acceleration = speed/time, the units are in mph/h which is *miles per hour per hour*. (Answers on page 309.)

Sequences

A sequence is a series of numbers which is described by two things:

- a starting number
- a rule that tells you what the "gap" is between each number

The easiest sequence in maths is 1, 2, 3, 4, 5... and so on. This sequence starts at 1 and the rule is + 1. In other words, as you move along each number you add 1. To describe this using algebra, you would say $n \Rightarrow n + 1$. This is a way of saying that whatever number you've got, the next one is the same plus one.

Not quite. Here are some more sequences and underneath the difference between the numbers is shown:

$$2 \quad\quad 5 \quad\quad 8 \quad\quad 11 \quad\quad 14...$$
$$+3 \quad\quad +3 \quad\quad +3 \quad\quad +3$$

Here you can see you start with 2 and the rule is + 3 or $n \Rightarrow n + 3$.

$$18 \quad\quad 11 \quad\quad 4 \quad\quad -3 \quad\quad -10...$$
$$-7 \quad\quad -7 \quad\quad -7 \quad\quad -7$$

Here you start with 18 and the rule is – 7 or $n \Rightarrow n - 7$.

$$4 \quad 5 \quad 8 \quad 13 \quad 20 \quad 29...$$
$$+1 \quad +3 \quad +5 \quad +7 \quad +9 \quad \text{this line shows the first differences}$$
$$+2 \quad +2 \quad +2 \quad +2 \quad \text{this line shows the second differences}$$

If you had to describe this sequence in words you might say "Start with 4. Add 1, then add 3 then 5 then 7. Keep going, adding on two more each time."

Sequences that use adding are called **arithmetic** sequences. There are also sequences that use multiplying which are called **geometric** sequences.

$$3 \qquad 9 \qquad 27 \qquad 81 \qquad 243...$$
$$\times 3 \qquad \times 3 \qquad \times 3 \qquad \times 3$$

Here the rule is × 3 or $n \Rightarrow 3n$.

Some sequences use both adding *and* multiplying! Look at this one:

$$4 \qquad 10 \qquad 28 \qquad 82 \qquad 244...$$
$$+ 6 \qquad + 18 \qquad + 54 \qquad + 162$$
$$\times 3 \qquad \times 3 \qquad \times 3$$

The first line of differences don't indicate much, but when you look carefully you'll see that each difference is three times as big as the last. This means that × 3 comes into the rule somewhere, so let's experiment by trying the rule $n \Rightarrow 3n$ with the first number in the sequence.

We start with 4 so using $n \Rightarrow 3n$ the next number would be 4 × 3 = 12. This is too big as the next number in the sequence is 10. So maybe you have to multiply by 3 and then subtract 2 each time? The rule would be $n \Rightarrow 3n - 2$.

Starting with 4 we get (4 × 3) − 2 = 10 so that works fine.

Now try with 10 and we get (10 × 3) − 2 = 28. YES! Just what we wanted.

Try 28 and we get (28 × 3) − 2 = 82, and if we try 82 we get (82 × 3) − 2 = 244.

The rule $n \Rightarrow 3n - 2$ works, so now we can describe this sequence as starting with 4 and the rule is × 3 − 2.

F: Finding the rules for sequences
The last example shows how to go about it. You write out the sequence just like the ones we've already seen, then underneath

you write out a line showing the differences between the numbers. If this doesn't show anything obvious, then write out a second line. Look out for adding/subtracting the same number each time, or multiplying by the same number.

TOP TIP
Always make sure that you know whether the sequence involves adding or multiplying. If the numbers look like they are about to suddenly get massive (or suddenly turn into little fractions) then the sequence involves multiplying, but these don't usually turn up in exams.

There are also other odd tricks in sequences. You might come across the famous **Fibonacci Sequence** which goes like this:

$$1 \quad 1 \quad 2 \quad 3 \quad 5 \quad 8 \quad 13 \quad 21 \quad 34...$$
$$+0 \quad +1 \quad +1 \quad +2 \quad +3 \quad +5 \quad +8 \quad +13$$

Notice how the first line of differences has 1, 1, 2, 3, 5… which is the same as the original sequence! In fact each number in the sequence comes from adding the previous two numbers together! 1 + 1 = 2 then 1 + 2 = 3 then 2 + 3 = 5 and so on. Can you work out the next two numbers in the sequence? (Answers on page 310.)

I: Sequences of squares, cubes and triangle numbers
Squares
If you write out the sequence 1^2, 2^2, 3^2, 4^2, 5^2, 6^2, 7^2… and work out the values you get **1, 4, 9, 16, 25, 36, 49…** Let's see if they form a pattern.

```
1       4       9       16      25      36      49...
   + 3     + 5     + 7     + 9     + 11    + 13
      + 2     + 2     + 2     + 2     + 2
```

There it is! A constant second difference of + 2.

Cubes

The sequence starts 1^3, 2^3, 3^3, 4^3, 5^3, 6^3, 7^3... and the values are **1, 8, 27, 64, 125, 216, 343**... Here's what happens when we break this sequence down:

```
1       8       27      64      125     216     343...
   + 7     + 19    + 37    + 61    + 91    + 127
      + 12    + 18    + 24    + 30    + 36
         + 6     + 6     + 6     + 6
```

With cubes there is a constant *third* difference of + 6.

Triangle numbers

The sequence starts: **1, 3, 6, 10, 15, 21, 28**... so here we go:

```
1       3       6       10      15      21      28...
   + 2     + 3     + 4     + 5     + 6     + 7
      + 1     + 1     + 1     + 1     + 1
```

Triangle numbers have a constant second difference of + 1.

F: Using algebra for sequences

Suppose you have a sequence that starts **3, 8, 13, 18, 23, 28**... (can you spot the rule for this?) and you need to know the 38th number in the sequence? It's a bit dull having to write the whole sequence out until you get the number you want, so algebra gives quicker methods. The first way of saving time is instead of having to write out long things like "the first number in the sequence" or "the thirty-eighth number in the sequence" we use as few letters as possible. How about this:

t a number or term in the sequence

t_1 the first number in the sequence

t_{23} the twenty-third number in the sequence

Already these abbreviations are going to save us a lot of effort!

Look at the sequence 3, 8, 13, 18, 23, 28... again. We can see that the first number is 3, so we could put $t_1 = 3$. We could also put $t_2 = 8$ and $t_3 = 13$ and so on. By now you might have realized that $t_1 + 5 = t_2$ (because $3 + 5 = 8$) and $t_2 + 5 = t_3$ (because $8 + 5 = 13$) and $t_3 + 5 = t_4$. The gap between each term is always $+ 5$ and this tells us that we've got an arithmetic sequence.

We could use algebra to describe this sequence as $t_n = 5n - 2$. t_n is called the **general term or nth term** and the n can be any number you like. If we just wanted to know the first number in the sequence, we make $n = 1$. We get $t_1 = (5 \times 1) - 2 = 3$ which is what we expected. Let's check the fourth number: $t_4 = (5 \times 4) - 2 = 18$. The good bit is that if we wanted the 38th number in the sequence we just write $t_{38} = (5 \times 38) - 2 = 190 - 2 = 188$ and we haven't had to write the whole sequence out!

If you are given the general term of a sequence, it's easy to work out the value of any specific terms they ask for. Here's a real tough one: $t_n = 7 - 3 \times 2^{n+1}$. Whatever terms they ask for, just change n and work them out. So if they wanted the 8th term in this sequence, you change n into 8 and put $t_8 = 7 - 3 \times 2^{8+1} = 7 - 3 \times 2^9 = 7 - 3 \times 512 = 7 - 1536 = -1529$. (Remember to do the multiplication before the subtraction.)

F: Working out the nth term: arithmetic sequences

When you are trying to find the formula for the nth term of an arithmetic sequence, you usually end up *multiplying* the constant difference by n.

Look at this sequence: **41, 37, 33, 29, 25, 21...**

- First you can see that you have to subtract 4 each time, so -4 is the constant difference. Our formula should contain $-4 \times n$ which is the same as $-4n$.
- Now we need to adjust our formula so that the first number in the sequence is correct. Suppose we just had $t_n = -4n$ then for the first number we make $n = 1$ so $t_1 = -4$. That's no good at the moment because the sequence is supposed to start with $t_1 = 41$.
- Now we ask ourselves: what do we have to add to -4 to make it into 41? We have to add 45 so let's improve our formula to say $t_n = -4n + 45$.
- Test the formula to see if it produces the terms in the original sequence:

$$t_1 = -4 + 45 = 41 \text{ YES!}$$

$$t_2 = -(4 \times 2) + 45 = -8 + 45 = 37 \text{ YES AGAIN!}$$

If you go on and test a few more terms, you'll see we've done it.

Now we've seen how the whole thing works, this is what it all boils down to:

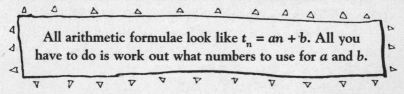

All arithmetic formulae look like $t_n = an + b$. All you have to do is work out what numbers to use for a and b.

Exam questions on sequences are often dressed up as real problems. Try this one:

> **Your mad Auntie Carol leaves you £550,000 and you limit yourself to spending £7,000 a week. How much have you got left after six weeks? How much is left after 20 weeks? Write a formula so you can work out how much you've got left after *n* weeks.**

Answers on page 310.

H: Working out your own nth terms: geometric sequences

With geometric sequences your formula will include something to a power of *n*. This sounds ghastly but let's try: **2, 10, 50, 250, 1250**...

First we'll write it out so we can see what the differences are:

2   10   50   250   1250

    8   40   200   1000

     × 5   × 5   × 5

As you can see the difference is five times bigger at every step. This means our formula will include 5^n.

- Let's do a test formula $t_n = 5^n$.
- We'll try t_1 and get $t_1 = 5^1 = 5$. We need to adjust our test formula because t_1 should really be 2. *Because this is a geometric sequence, we don't add or subtract. Instead we make our adjustment by multiplying.* So what do we multiply 5 by to get 2? The answer is $\frac{2}{5}$ so use this to improve the formula.
- The improved formula is $t_n = \frac{2}{5} \times 5^n$. Let's try this for t_2. We get $t_2 = \frac{2}{5} \times 5^2 = \frac{2}{5} \times 25 = \frac{50}{5} = 10$. YES!
- Try $t_n = \frac{2}{5} \times 5^n$ for the other terms yourself. You should find it works.

So the formula is $\frac{2}{5} \times 5^n$, but here's the slick bit. We can write this as $2 \times \frac{5^n}{5}$ and if we simplify this we get $2 \times 5^{n-1}$. So for our sequence we can say that $t_n = 2 \times 5^{n-1}$.

Very occasionally this sort of sequence might turn up: **4, 1, $\frac{1}{4}$, $\frac{1}{16}$, $\frac{1}{64}$ ...**

You can see the sequence is rapidly disappearing into tiny fractions so you can be sure it's geometric. As the terms are getting smaller, you will be *dividing* by the same number each time and you should be able to spot that here it's $\div 4$ which is the same as $\times \frac{1}{4}$.

- Our first test formula will give us $t_n = (\frac{1}{4})^n = \frac{1}{4^n}$.
- We try the first term and get $t_1 = \frac{1}{4}$.
  What do we need to multiply this by to get $t_1 = 4$? Answer: 16.
- The improved formula is $16 \times \frac{1}{4^n} = \frac{16}{4^n}$.

If you try this formula it will be correct, but we can make it smarter! Because $16 = 4^2$, the formula is $\frac{4^2}{4^n}$ so you could say the formula is $t_n = 4^{(2-n)}$.

H: Other sequences

Some sequences don't exactly fit arithmetic or geometric progressions. Look at this sequence: $\frac{1}{3}, \frac{3}{5}, \frac{5}{7}, \frac{7}{9}, \frac{9}{11}, \frac{11}{13}$ ... It has an obvious pattern but how do we make a formula? The way to do it is to make a formula for the tops of the fraction and a separate formula for the bottoms. Let's write it out clearly:

$n =$	1	2	3	4	5	6
t_n (tops only) =	1	3	5	7	9	11
t_n (bottoms only) =	3	5	7	9	11	13

The tops are a simple arithmetic progression, with a constant difference of $+ 2$, so the formula will have $2n$ in it. When you've tried it for $n = 1$ you'll find the formula for the tops is $2n - 1$.

The bottoms are also arithmetic progression and there's a short cut here. Each number on the bottom is always 2 more than the number on the top, so the formula for the bottom numbers is $(2n - 1) + 2$ which is $2n + 1$.

The formula for the sequence is therefore: $\frac{2n-1}{2n+1}$

Finally, let's look at the sequence $\frac{1}{2}, \frac{2}{4}, \frac{3}{8}, \frac{4}{16}$ ... Here the bottoms are in geometric progression which works out to be 2^n, but the tops are just n by itself. For example the 6th term will have a 6 on top. The formula for the whole sequence is $\frac{n}{2^n}$.

Now try these. Work out the formulae for the following sequences:
a) 2 5 8 11 14   **b)** 6 12 24 48

Answers on page 310.

I need to get into Shape

F: Useful words

Before we get into the drawing bit of maths, let's be sure of what we're talking about. Most of these words will be obvious to you, but some might not be, so check that you know them all.

Point
An exact position, it has no size.

Line
A distance connecting two points. It has a **length** that can be measured, but *a line does not have any width*.

A "straight line" is the *shortest* distance between two points. When two lines meet, they meet at a point. A straight line is 180°.

STRAIGHT LINE = 180° ———⌒———

Right angle   A 90° angle, usually indicated by a little box.

RIGHT = 90°
Angle

Acute angle   An angle of less than 90°.

ACUTE < 90°
Angle

Obtuse angle   An angle greater than 90° but less than 180°.

< 90° OBTUSE < 180°
        Angle

Reflex angle   An angle greater than 180°.

REFLEX > 180°
Angle

Supplementary angles Two or more angles that together add up to 180°.

Included angle   Where two lines meet, the angle between them is the "included" angle.

Perpendicular   If two lines meet at a right angle, they are said to be perpendicular.

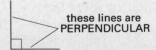

these lines are
PERPENDICULAR

Parallel	Straight lines that are always exactly the same distance apart are parallel: usually marked with arrowheads.

PARALLEL lines

Perimeter	The line round the edge of an area.
Volume	A solid with length, width and depth.
Quadrilateral	Any shape with four straight sides.
Polygon	A shape with any number of straight sides.
Regular polygon	A shape with all sides equal in length and all angles equal.
Horizontal line	A line going across the page.
Vertical line	A line going "up and down" the page. Vertical is always perpendicular to horizontal. Sometimes people talk about a vertical line when they mean a perpendicular line.
Locus	A locus is a line of points that follows a set of rules. (When you've got more than one locus they are called "loci" in the same way as words like radius and focus. But not bus, which are "buses" not "bi".)

Circle	The locus of all points the same distance from a centre point.

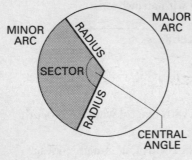 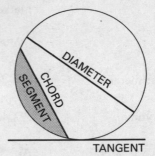

Circumference	The length around the outside of the circle.
Arc	A section of the circumference (a **minor arc** is less than halfway round, a **major arc** is more than halfway round).
Radius	The distance from the centre point to the circumference. More than one radius are called radii which is the only English word that ends in "ii". (You never know when a fact like that will come in useful.)
Central angle	The angle at the centre between two radii.
Diameter	A straight line right across the circle through the centre. The length of the diameter is always 2 × radius.
Chord	A straight line across a circle that does not pass through the centre.

Tangent   A straight line that touches the circumference of a circle at one point.

OK, I understand the words. Now what do I do with them?

Labelling sides and angles in triangles

Usually the corners of triangles are labelled with capital letters such as A, B and C. The sides are known as AB, BC and CA.

When there's just a simple triangle on a page the angles can be called A, B and C. However, when drawings get more complicated the angles are called after the two sides that make them, so the angle between AB and CA will be BÂC.

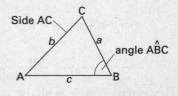

Side AC

angle AB̂C

Later on, you'll find that sometimes the sides are labelled with small letters a, b, c. Side a is opposite angle A, b opposite B and c opposite C.

F: How angles add up

Two angles next to each other on a straight line always add up to 180°. $a + b = 180°$

Triangles

The three angles in a triangle always add up to 180°. You can easily see this because if you cut a triangle out of paper and tear the three corners off, when you put them together you get a straight line.

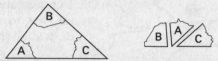

For any triangle we can say that angles A + B + C = 180°. This is useful as it means that if you know two angles of a triangle you can always work out the third one.

If you extend one of the sides of a triangle a bit, you get an **external angle**.

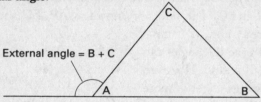

External angle = B + C

This external angle is always equal to the opposite angles added together. In this case A + (B + C) = 180° because it's a straight line.

Triangles can be described in the following ways:

Scalene   All sides different, all angles different.

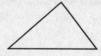

Isosceles   Two sides the same length (usually marked with a dash). Two angles the same.

Equilateral   All sides the same length (usually marked with two dashes). All angles = 60°.

Right-angled   Any triangle with a right angle in it. (Can be scalene or isosceles.)

Once you know about triangles, then everything else falls nicely into place.

Well I don't see how they help me with my history exam.

Quadrilaterals
You can split ANY quadrilateral into two triangles.

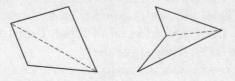

As there are 180° in each triangle, you can see that there are 2 × 180° = 360° in any quadrilateral.

Polygons with more sides

You can split any polygon into triangles. For every extra side the polygon has, you need one more triangle.

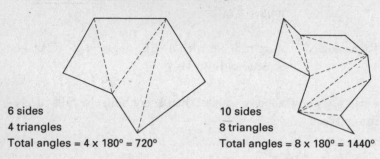

6 sides
4 triangles
Total angles = 4 × 180° = 720°

10 sides
8 triangles
Total angles = 8 × 180° = 1440°

To find out what all the angles in a polygon add up to, you work out the smallest number of triangles it splits into and multiply by 180. Otherwise you can just subtract 2 from the number of sides and multiply by 180 and there's a little formula for this:

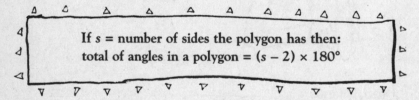

If s = number of sides the polygon has then:
total of angles in a polygon = $(s - 2) \times 180°$

F: Names of polygons

You should know the names of the five most common polygons: **Triangle** (3 sides), **Quadrilateral** (4 sides), **Pentagon** (5 sides), **Hexagon** (6 sides), **Octagon** (8 sides).

And just to warn you, you might also come across: **Septagon** or **Heptagon** (7 sides), **Nonagon** (9 sides), **Decagon** (10 sides), **Dodecagon** (12 sides).

F: Regular polygon angles

We've already seen what the angles of a polygon add up to. All the corners of a regular polygon touch a circle and it can be broken into a set of identical isosceles triangles which meet in the middle. In the diagram all the angles marked *a* are equal. Notice that the interior angles of the polygon all = 2*a*.

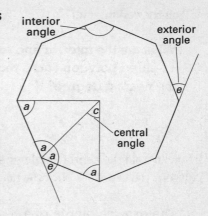

If you look at one of the triangles you can see that 2*a* + *c* = 180°. If you look at the extended side, you can also see that 2*a* + *e* = 180°. Therefore *c* = *e*. This gives us three useful facts:

- In a regular polygon the central angle = the exterior angle = 360° divided by the number of sides.

- Exterior angle + interior angle = 180°.

- The exterior angles add up to 360°.

Here's a typical question:

> **What are the interior and exterior angles of a regular nonagon?**

A nonagon has 9 sides, so first work out the central angle. Easy, it's just 360° ÷ 9 = 40°. This is the same as the exterior angle. The interior angle is 180° − 40° = 140°.

You try working out:

What are the interior and exterior angles of a regular 11-sided polygon and a regular 20-sided polygon to the nearest degree?

Answers on page 310.

If you are told the central angle or the external angle of a regular polygon, you can work out how many sides it has.

The external angle of a regular polygon is 24°. How many sides does it have?

The exterior angles are all the same and add up to 360°. So how many 24s are there in 360? Easy it's 360 ÷ 24 = 15. This polygon has 15 sides.

F: When angles are equal

You should be aware of when equal angles turn up. In these diagrams all angles with the same letters are equal:

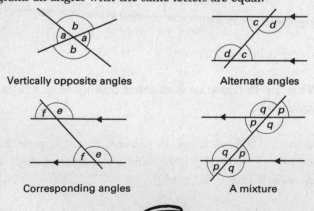

Vertically opposite angles   Alternate angles

Corresponding angles   A mixture

There are also lots of pairs which add up to 180° (which makes them supplementary angles): $a + b = 180°$, $c + d = 180°$, $e + f = 180°$, $p + q = 180°$.

Accurate Constructions

Make sure your ruler, set square and protractor have clean, smooth edges. Pencils should be sharp. Your eraser must be clean. The pencil or lead in your compasses must be fastened securely.

For accurate constructions: ALWAYS use a ruler to draw lines, ALWAYS use compasses to draw circles and when drawing exact angles ALWAYS use a protractor.

There are people in the past who have drawn all their lines and circles freehand in their exams and guessed at angles. They think they'll dazzle the examiner with a bit of cheeky charm by writing "Ooops, I haven't got a ruler" or "Sorry, I haven't got any compasses". They didn't get any marks either!

Keep it neat! Being tidy is worth the effort because it keeps the examiner on your side. Mess usually turns up when you have to rub something out, so try and avoid it when you can. Always use a clean eraser, don't sharpen pencils right to a pin point and don't press too hard on the paper.

You should also make sure your hands are clean before the exam. If your hands tend to get clammy (and most people's do during exams!) put a small loose piece of paper between the base of your hand and the page you're working on. As you move your hand over the page the loose piece should slide with it and stop everything looking grubby.

F: Using a protractor

Hopefully you know how to use a ruler and a pair of compasses to draw exact lines and circles, but some people find protractors a bit confusing.

To measure angles, you put the protractor on one of the lines so that the middle is exactly over the point of the angle. You then read off where the other line crosses the scale – but you'll see there are two numbers! A bit of common sense tells you that if the angle is less than 90° then read off the lower number. If it is higher than 90° read the higher number.

Reflex angles

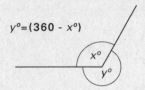

$y° = (360 - x°)$

If you needed to measure angle y, the easiest thing to do is measure x, then subtract it from 360°.

F: Scale drawings

You're likely to be asked to do accurate drawings and then take measurements to get answers. Here's a typical example:

> **A mad yak has two ropes attached to a ring in its collar. One rope is 10 m and one is 7 m, and they are fixed to stakes that are 11 m apart. What is the furthest distance the yak can charge in a straight line?**

If you happen to have some paper that's about 12 m square as well as a very long ruler, then you can draw this full scale. However, you'll be better off scaling the dimensions down and it's not a bad idea to do a quick doodle and see roughly what your finished diagram will look like. That way you can choose a sensible scale, and start your drawing in the right place on the paper. In this book we've used a scale of 5 mm : 1 m. As 5 mm is 200 times smaller than 1 m, you could also call your scale 1:200.

Off we go then. . .

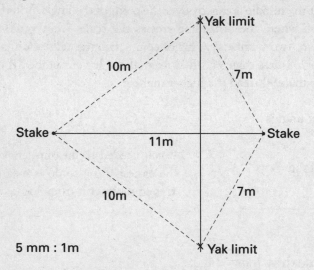

How did we do that? First the two stakes were drawn 55 mm apart. Next the compasses were set to 50 mm and two arcs drawn from the first stake. Then the compasses were set to 35 mm and two arcs drawn from the second stake. Finally the points where the arcs crossed were marked which shows the two limits to the yak's movements. Now the distance between them can be measured. It's about 62 mm.

TOP TIP
Don't forget to scale answers back up! You'll lose marks if you don't.

The yak would look pretty silly charging 62 mm, so obviously you have to convert this back to get an answer of 12·4 m.

TOP TIP

Only scale lengths, NOT angles. If you are given an angle of 28°, it is always 28° regardless of what scale you use.

Later on you might find you are drawing scale diagrams to represent things like speed. Just keep your head together, and to help both yourself and the examiner. . .

TOP TIP

Always write in what scale you are using, and make sure everything on the same drawing is to the same scale.

So suppose the question about the yak wanted you to draw in a daisy that was growing 37 cm from the left hand stake, you need to convert this to 0·37 m. When you draw this to scale, you would end up making a mark 1·85 cm from the stake.

If you're still unsure, there's a bit more about scale and proportions back in the numbers chapter.

I: Drawing loci
Here's how to find some loci:

The locus of all points equidistant from a centre point.

Draw a circle. That's all there is to it.

The locus of all points equidistant from a line.

Draw a circle on each end of the line using the ends of the line as the centre point of your circles. Draw two straight lines parallel to the original to complete the shape as shown.

The locus of all points equidistant from two points.

Open your compasses to slightly over half the distance between the points. Draw arcs from each point that intersect each other at two places. Use your ruler to join the arc intersections up.

(Incidentally, you've just drawn the **perpendicular bisector** of the line joining the two original points, because it chops this line exactly in half at right angles.)

The locus of all points equidistant from two lines that meet at an angle.

Open your compasses, put the point on the angle and mark each line with an arc. (We'll call these marks *f* and *g* for now.) Put your compass point on *f* and draw a little arc roughly in the middle of the

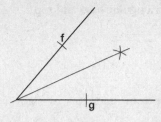

angle. *Keep your compasses open the same distance*. Put the compass point on point g and draw an arc to cut the second arc in the middle of the angle. Draw a straight line from the point of the angle to where the arcs meet. (This time you've **bisected the angle**.)

F: Solids

There are one or two lumps that you should know about, i.e. 3-D shapes, or **solids**.

Regular tetrahedron   Four sides, all equilateral triangles.

Cube   Six exactly equal square sides.

Cuboid   Six rectangular sides – opposite sides the same.

Cylinder   A "tube" or "bean can" with circular base and top and straight sides.

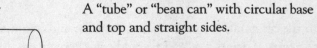

Triangular prism

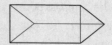

A "tube" with triangular base and top.

Any other prism

Same shape bottom and top, straight sides join the two.

It's worth practising how to draw these shapes, even just roughly. The knack is to make sure that the lines do not run on top of each other. If in doubt, just do the whole of one side first (the most peculiarly shaped one if necessary), then draw the rest in.

Nets

A net is a flat drawing showing all the sides of a solid. If you cut the drawing out you could fold along the lines and tape the edges up and make the solid. You should be aware of which edges join together when looking at a net.

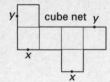

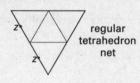

In the diagrams, if you assembled the cube and the tetrahedron, the pairs of points x, y, and z would come together.

Symmetry

F: There are two types of symmetry – reflective and rotational.

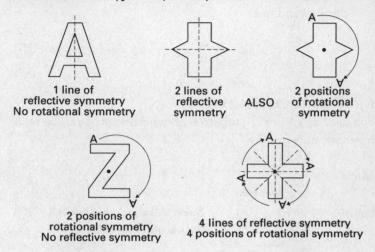

1 line of
reflective symmetry
No rotational symmetry

2 lines of
reflective
symmetry

ALSO

2 positions
of rotational
symmetry

2 positions of
rotational symmetry
No reflective symmetry

4 lines of reflective symmetry
4 positions of rotational symmetry

- If a shape has **reflective symmetry**, you can fold it down the middle and the two sides will fall exactly over each other. If the shape was cut out of card and turned over, you wouldn't know. Some shapes have more than one line of reflective symmetry.

- If a shape has **rotational symmetry** and you cut it out of card and pin it to the wall, you can't tell if it's the right way up! Some shapes have two positions of rotational symmetry, others have more.

Some shapes have both reflective AND rotational symmetry. You may well be given shapes like these and be asked to draw in lines of reflective symmetry, or say how may positions of rotational symmetry they have.

Consider scalene, isosceles and equilateral triangles. What reflective and rotational symmetry does each have?

Answers on page 310.

F: Different quadrilaterals

You need to know the properties of the shapes that can be made with four straight sides:

Shape

Square

Sides: All equal. **Angles:** All = 90°.
Symmetry: 4 ref 4 rot.

Rectangle

Sides: Opposites equal.
Angles: All = 90°.
Symmetry: 2 ref 2 rot.

Rhombus

Sides: All equal, opposites parallel.
Angles: Opposites equal.
Symmetry: 2 ref 2 rot.

Parallelogram

Sides: Opposites equal and parallel.
Angles: Opposites equal.
Symmetry: 2 rot.

Kite 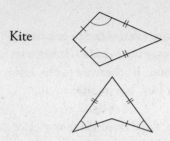 **Sides:** Touching pairs equal.
Angles: One pair of opposites equal.
Symmetry: 1 ref.

Regular
trapezium 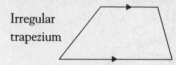 **Sides:** One opposite pair equal,
other pair parallel. **Angles:** Two
equal pairs. **Symmetry:** 1 ref.

Irregular
trapezium  **Sides:** One opposite pair parallel.
Angles: None equal.
Symmetry: None.

Irregular quadrilateral Does not fall into any of the above
categories

Congruence

This is when two shapes (or solids) are exactly alike. There are
three things to check before you can say they are congruent:

- Is there enough information to draw each shape accurately? If
  a shape does not have enough information for you to draw it,
  then you cannot say the shape is congruent to any other shape.

- Make sure that any given line lengths are connected to the
  same angles in both shapes.

● Make sure that angles that are next to each other in one shape are also next to each other in the congruent shape. (It helps to remember that with many shapes, if there is only one unmarked angle, you can work out how big it is.)

If a measurement or angle is not the same *or in the wrong place* then the shapes are not congruent. Although congruency can apply to any sort of shape or lump, you really only need to understand what happens with the simplest shapes, so let's see how they might test you. (*Ignore the shapes of the drawings, these are deliberately wrong so the answers are not obvious!* For instance in triangle A the "6" side looks as long as the "11" side. Just concentrate on the numbers given.)

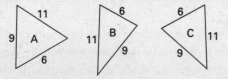

Which of these shapes is the odd one out?

If you look at triangles A and B , you'll see that they are the same, but B has just been rotated a bit. This counts as being congruent.

Triangle C has the numbers going round the other way – so it's been "flipped over". However, this still counts as being congruent so in fact there isn't an odd one out here.

Which of these shapes is the matching pair?

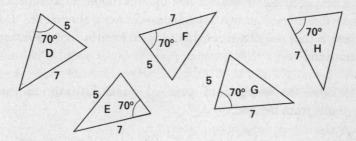

First you'll notice that triangle H only shows one side and one angle. If you had to draw it, this is not enough information, so we certainly don't know enough about it to say whether it's congruent or not. If in doubt – say not. For the others, you have to see which sides the 70° angle is opposite. Triangle D has the 70° angle opposite to the "7" side, and E has it opposite the "5" side. F and G both have the angle opposite the unmarked side, so these two are congruent.

Which of *these* shapes is the matching pair?

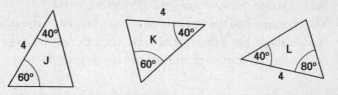

Go on try it yourself – but watch out for the diabolically cunning trap! (Answers on page 310.)

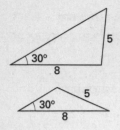

Watch out! Even though the given measurements are the same, you cannot say that these two triangles are definitely congruent. Remember that when constructing triangles, if you have two sides and the non-included angle it can produce two completely different shapes. In this diagram they are drawn roughly to scale to show how different they could be.

Find the congruent pair of quadrilaterals in the diagram below:

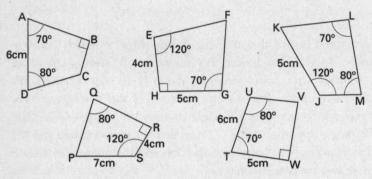

You can do this by a process of elimination:

- Which shape does not give enough information?
- Which shape has the angles in a different order to the others?
- Which shape has a given length between the wrong angles?
- So which pair are congruent? (Answers on page 310.)

A little trick examiners sometimes try: they give angle sizes and side lengths as letters rather than numbers. Just treat them as if they were numbers so these two...

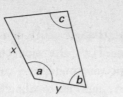

...would be congruent. There's enough information and everything matches up.

Similar shapes

We've just see that if two shapes have the same angles and the same sides then they are congruent. However, if two shapes just have the same angles, they are **similar**.

PQR = 1·5 × JKL

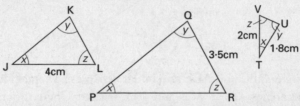

Here J = P, K = Q and L = R. The triangles JKL and PQR are therefore similar even though PQR is plainly larger.

In the triangles JKL and TUV, J = T, K = U and L = T so these triangles are similar too, even though TUV is rotated and a mirror image. It also follows that triangle PQR is similar to TUV. To make this clear the equal angles in each triangle are marked x, y and z.

The useful bit is that the sides opposite the equal angles are all in ratio. If we are told that triangle PQR is 1·5 the scale of JKL, and we know a few measurements, we can go on to calculate the sides of one triangle from the other. For example, when we compare the sides opposite angle y we can say that PR = 1·5 × JL. As we know that JL = 4 cm, we can work out that PR = 1·5 × 4 = 6 cm. QR = 3·5 cm so we can work out that KL = $\frac{3·5}{1·5}$ = 2·33 cm.

We are not told what scale triangle TUV is to the others. However, we can see that in TUV the side opposite angle y = 2 cm and in JKL the side opposite angle y = 4 cm. This makes TUV $\frac{2}{4}$ the scale of JKL, which simplifies to triangle TUV being half the scale of JKL.

Can you work out the length of VU, JK and PQ?

Answers on page 311.

Here's another way you might meet similar triangles:

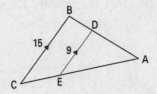

The triangles ABC and ADE are similar because the parallel lines show that angles AÊD = AĈB and ED̂A = CB̂A . Obviously angle A is the same for both. The lengths of the sides DE and BC give the ratios of the triangles as 9:15 which cancels down to 3:5. This is a good time for a quick reminder of how ratios work. The ratio of DA to BA is also 3:5, so if the length of BA was 5 km long, DA would be 3 km which would make BD 2 km. Therefore you can also say that the ratio of BD to BA = 2:5 and this is also the ratio of CE to CA.

Here's the sort of questions they might ask you about this diagram:

If EA = 15 what is CA? If BD = 8, what is DA?

Answers on page 311.

Pythagoras' theorem

I: He's possibly one of the oddest blokes who ever walked the planet followed by an adoring entourage, but this ancient Greek mathematician did come up with some amazing stuff and best known is his theorem:

> In any right-angled triangle, the square on the hypotenuse is equal to the sum of the squares on the other two sides.

$$a^2 + b^2 = c^2$$

The "hypotenuse" is the longest side and the diagrams explain what's going on. In all the triangles, $a^2 + b^2 = c^2$. If you prefer to think of this visually, the area of the two smaller squares together is equal to that of the bigger square.

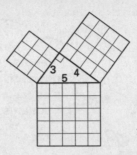

The "3,4,5" triangle is the very simplest example of this rule and if you work out $3^2 + 4^2 = 5^2$ you get $9 + 16 = 25$ so it works.

TOP TIP
Always look out for 3, 4, 5 triangles. They come in all over the place – although they may be disguised! If you see a 9, 12, 15 triangle it's the same as a 3, 4, 5 triangle but the sides are all three times longer. Have a look back at the similar triangles ABC and ADE on page 182 and spot the right angles!

I: Finding the "third side"

Thanks to Pythagoras, if you are given two sides of a right-angled triangle you can always find the third. Here's a typical example:

A 7 m ladder is leaning against a wall. The bottom of the ladder is 2·5 m away from the wall. How far up the

wall is the top of the ladder? Solve this with Pythagoras' theorem and also an accurate drawing.

Do a quick "thumbnail" drawing first. It only has to be rough, just so that you can see where your measurements go.

If we call the height up the wall w then: $2{\cdot}5^2 + w^2 = 7^2$.

So $w^2 = 7^2 - 2{\cdot}5^2 = 49 - 6{\cdot}25 = 42{\cdot}75$. Therefore $w = 6{\cdot}54$ m (to two decimal places).

Now try doing a scale drawing as accurately as possible and see what you get.

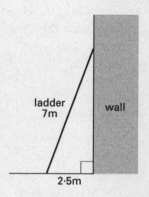

I: **Hidden right angles**

> **Five triangles have sides: 4, 7, 9; 6, 9, 11; 5, 12, 13; 7, 8, 17; 8, 14, 16. Which one is right-angled? (And which one is NOT a triangle?)**

In case they try to catch you out, obviously the two shorter sides of a triangle must add up to more than the longest side or they couldn't meet! In other words $a + b > c$. You'll see one of these triangles cannot actually exist!

To find the right-angled triangle, just try putting the numbers into the equation $a^2 + b^2 = c^2$ and see if it works. (Remember that c is always the longest side.) In the first case you get $4^2 + 7^2 = 9^2$ which comes to $16 + 49 = 81$. Of course this is not correct so the triangle does not have a right angle. But which one does? (Answers on page 311.)

I: Pythagoras' theorem and co-ordinates

Sometimes the information in a question is given as graph co-ordinates like this:

Calculate the length of the line from (− 2, 4) to (4,1).

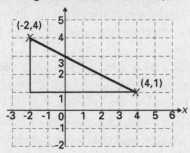

As you can see, this is just asking for the hypotenuse of a right-angled triangle, with one side being the x length, and the other being the y length. From the diagram you can see that the length of the x side is 6 units and the y side is 3 units. So what answer do you get? (Answer on page 311.)

Trigonometry

Triggy what?

I: Trigonometry is a nasty word, but don't be scared. Life is jollier if you just call it "trig" and it gets even more jolly when you realize that trig is one great big mathematical short cut. Pythagoras showed how the three sides of a right-angled triangle are related, and trigonometry goes on to show how the angles get involved. Obviously one of the angles is always going to be 90° but it's the other two we're interested in. Look at this:

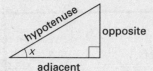

If you pick one of the two smaller angles, this diagram shows what the sides are called:

Hypotenuse This is always the longest side of a right-angled triangle.

Opposite This side is opposite the angle you're dealing with.

Adjacent This is the side that touches the angle.

The angle "x°" can be described by a ratio called a "sine" which is usually written as "sin" to save hours of time. "Sin x°" is equal to the length of the opposite side divided by the length of the hypotenuse. Usually people just say:

$$\sin x° = \frac{\text{opposite}}{\text{hypotenuse}}$$

What the "sin" bit does is convert the degrees into a fraction, and if you're unsure about this here's a little experiment:

- Draw a right-angled triangle with a 30° angle. The triangle can be as big or small as you like.
- Find out what sin 30° is. You can do this by putting 30 into your calculator and then pressing [sin]. You should get 0·5. (If

not then see the calculator bit below.)
- Measure the opposite side of your triangle and divide it by the length of the hypotenuse. You will also get 0·5.

It doesn't matter how big or small your triangle is, this will work! Any right-angled triangle with a 30° angle has an opposite side that is half the length of its hypotenuse.

Calculators and trig
Two things to make absolutely sure of:

- Always make sure your calculator is working in "degrees". Sometimes there is a switch or other way of making them work in "radians" or "grads". Check with the instructions!
- Check that pushing 30 [sin] gives you 0·5. (Notice that for sin 30° you push the [30] first and then the [sin].) If your calculator doesn't give you 0·5 then look at the instructions to see if your calculator needs a different way of pushing the buttons. In other words, make sure you can work the thing!

I: Sin, cos and tan
As well as sines, there are two other common ratios used in right-angled triangles: "cosine" and "tangent" which are far better known as "cos" and "tan". Here are all three together:

$$\sin x° = \frac{\text{opposite}}{\text{hypotenuse}} \qquad \cos x° = \frac{\text{adjacent}}{\text{hypotenuse}} \qquad \tan x° = \frac{\text{opposite}}{\text{adjacent}}$$

188

You've got to know these three so if they give you any trouble, try the most utterly stupid method: think of committing an evil SIN such as chucking a bucket of water at Windsor Castle. The queen will doubtless stick her head out of the window and shout...

...Hey, Phil, there's someone down there trying to SOAK OUR TOWER.

The last bit you spell like this: SOH CAH TOA which reminds you that $S = \frac{O}{H}$ $C = \frac{A}{H}$ $T = \frac{O}{A}$. Stupid enough for you? At least you'll never forget it.

I: Finding the sides of right-angled triangles

The trick of trig is knowing whether to use sin, cos or tan so let's dive in with a tough one and see how it works:

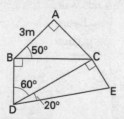

This fancy shape has three right-angled triangles: ABC, BCD and CDE. To be awkward let's suppose that we have to find the length of side CE. First we'll need to work out BC, then DC and then we can get CE.

BC This is the hypotenuse of triangle ABC. We are given the angle A$\hat{B}$C as 50° and the adjacent side AB as 3 m. Because the two sides we're dealing with are adjacent and hypotenuse, we use cos: cos 50° = $\frac{AB}{BC}$ = $\frac{3}{BC}$.

Swap this round and get: BC = $\frac{3}{\cos 50°}$ = 4·667 m.

You should make sure you can do this sort of sum on your calculator! On most calculators you would push 3 ÷ 50 [cos] = and that would give you the answer. (Check this on your calculator right now. Go on, do it!) However, some are different, so make sure you know what you are doing.

If in ANY doubt, then do the sum in stages by getting a value for cos 50° and putting it in first like this: BC = $\frac{3}{\cos 50°}$ = $\frac{3}{0·643}$ = 4·667 m.

TOP TIP
When giving answers, try to remember to write down the units of measurement! Otherwise you'll lose marks.

Here we were told the original side AB was 3 m. Our answer is also a length in metres, so even if you don't write "m" through your calculations, it shows a bit of class if you remember to put it in at the end.

She remembered to put in the metres!

> **TOP TIP**
> Unless told otherwise, round sin, cos and tans to three decimal places.

DC We now look at triangle BCD. We want DC which is the hypotenuse, we're told that angle BD̂C is 60° and we've already worked out BC which is the opposite side. As opposite and hypotenuse are involved, we need to use sin 60°: $\sin 60° = \frac{BC}{DC}$ and therefore DC = $\frac{BC}{\sin 60°}$.

You try working this one out! (Answer on page 311.)

CE Finally we get to triangle CDE. We're told that angle CD̂E is 20°, you've just worked out what the adjacent side DC is and we need the opposite side CE. Adjacent and opposite means that we're using tan: $\tan 20° = \frac{CE}{DC}$ and so CE = DC × tan 20°

Use your answer for DC and see what you get. Answer on page 311.

I: Values for sin, cos and tan

The hypotenuse is the longest side of a triangle, so of course it is always bigger than the opposite or adjacent. This means that values for sin and cos are ALWAYS less than 1.

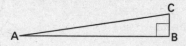

In this triangle angle A is almost 0°. You can see that the opposite side BC is almost 0 in length. If angle A really was 0°, then BC would have zero length. Therefore: $\sin 0° = \frac{BC}{AC} = \frac{0}{AC} = 0$.

You can also see that if angle A was reduced right down to 0° then angle C would get bigger until it reached 90°. (If this happened the side BC would disappear to nothing and the "triangle" would become two equal lines on top of each other.) The opposite side to this 90° angle is AB. As points C and B would be on top of each other, line AB would be the same length as line AC. As AB = AC this gives us: $\sin 90° = \frac{AB}{AC} = \frac{AC}{AC} = 1$.

Cos works the other way round and you get: $\cos 0° = \frac{AB}{AC} = \frac{AC}{AC} = 1$ and $\cos 90° = \frac{BC}{AC} = \frac{0}{AC} = 0$.

If you think tan through, you find that: $\tan 0° = \frac{BC}{AB} = \frac{0}{AB} = 0$ and $\tan 90° = \frac{AB}{BC} = \frac{AB}{0} = \propto$ (infinity).

Just for interest, when AB = BC you get an isosceles triangle, so angles A and C are both 45°. This gives the result: $\tan 45° = 1$.

Fascinating!

I: Finding the angles of right-angled triangles

If you are given any two sides of a right-angled triangle, you can use trig to work out the angles:

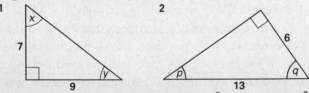

- In triangle 1 you can see that $\tan x° = \frac{9}{7}$ and $\tan y° = \frac{7}{9}$.
- In triangle 2 you can see that $\sin p° = \frac{6}{13}$ and $\cos q° = \frac{6}{13}$.

To get values for these things, you need to use $\sin^{-1}$, $\cos^{-1}$ and $\tan^{-1}$ on your calculator, so make sure you know how to do this. With most calculators you have to push an "inverse" or "2nd function" button and then use sin, cos or tan. Sorry, but this book can't help you here, you've got to find out for yourself what your calculator does.

TOP TIP
Check that you can do $\sin^{-1}$, $\cos^{-1}$ and $\tan^{-1}$ on your calculator. If you put in [0·5] and then [$\sin^{-1}$] your calculator should give an answer of 30°. If you try [0·5] and [$\cos^{-1}$] you should get 60° and with [0·5] and [$\tan^{-1}$] you should get 26·565°.

To work out the value for $x°$ in triangle 1 you need to work through $\tan x° = \frac{9}{7}$. First put "9 ÷ 7 =" into the calculator and get 1·286. Now you push the $\tan^{-1}$ button (or whatever your calculator needs you to do) and you get 52·13. This is the answer: $x = 52·13°$.

TOP TIP
As always, have a rough guess at what to expect first! Suppose you put 1·286 into the calculator and then tried $\tan^{-1}$ and got 0·022. This means that the angle x is 0·022° which is ridiculously small, and suggests that you've worked out tan instead of $\tan^{-1}$. You can see from the drawing that x has to be just over halfway to 90°, so you need a number in the 45–60 region. Have another go.

Now try and work out values for y, p and q in the two triangles. Of course you can check them afterwards because $x + y = 90$ and $p + q = 90$. (Answers on page 311.)

> **TOP TIP**
> Remember: if you are finding the lengths of sides, you use sin, cos or tan. If you are finding how many degrees in an angle, use $\sin^{-1}$, $\cos^{-1}$ or $\tan^{-1}$.

H: The sine rule for ANY triangle

There are some uses for trig that involve triangles without right angles. If a triangle doesn't have a right angle of course there is no hypotenuse, and so we usually just deal with the "opposite" side to an angle. There's one thing you can say about any triangle and that is: the bigger an angle is, then the bigger the opposite side will be. In terms of maths this is rather cutely described in this odd-looking formula:

$$\frac{a}{\sin A} = \frac{b}{\sin B} = \frac{c}{\sin C}$$

If you like you can turn the whole lot upside down like this:

$$\frac{\sin A}{a} = \frac{\sin B}{b} = \frac{\sin C}{c}$$

(You'll be given this formula in the exam – you just need to know how to work it.)

The main thing to notice is that side *a* is the side opposite angle A and so on. Of course most formulae only have two sides and one "equals" in the middle so it might seem a bit spooky that this has two "equals" and *three* sides! Don't worry because when you start swapping the letters for numbers, you can decide to miss one of the bits out as we'll see.

Here's the sort of thing this formula is useful for solving:

How long are sides *x* and *y*?

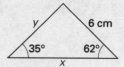

Before we go on, let's find the missing angle. It's $180° - 35° - 62° = 83°$. The formula tells us that: $\frac{6}{\sin 35°} = \frac{x}{\sin 83°} = \frac{y}{\sin 62°}$.

We'll get the *x* side first, so we just miss out the *y* part of the equation. It leaves us with: $\frac{6}{\sin 35°} = \frac{x}{\sin 83°}$.

And with a quick adjustment we get: $x = 6 \frac{\sin 83°}{\sin 35°}$.

Take it steadily with the calculator and we get x = 10·38 cm.

Your go. What do you get for *y*? (Just miss out the *x* bit and adjust the rest so that you have "y =" and then put the numbers in. (Answer on page 311.)

Now let's see how serious these sorts of questions can get. We're going to find all the sides and angles of this little beauty:

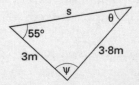

Don't worry if you haven't seen Greek letters like θ and ψ before. There's only a slim chance that you'll see them in an exam, and all they are doing is making a change from the usual letters. It's about as near as some mathematicians come to having a wild and crazy streak in their personalities.

Anyway, using the formula and seeing which angle is opposite which side, we can put: $\frac{\sin 55}{3 \cdot 8} = \frac{\sin \theta}{3} = \frac{\sin \psi}{s}$.

To start with we'll ignore the last sin ψ part of the equation because we don't know what either ψ or s is yet. Start by working out θ, so with a bit of a fiddle round we get: sin θ = 3 sin 55 ÷ 3·8 and so sin θ = 3 × 0·819 ÷ 3·8 = 0·647.

You then have to use $\sin^{-1}$ on 0·647 to get θ = 40·29.

So how do you work out s and ψ? This is the sort of thing they *love* seeing if you can spot in maths exams, so have a think about it, then see if you can get answers for both. (Answers on page 311.)

NOTE: In basic GCSE the sine rule is only used for "acute" triangles. It also works for triangles with an obtuse angle, but this makes life a bit trickier and so you don't need to worry about it.

H: The cosine rule for ANY triangle

You might think that you can get all the sides and angles you want from any triangle using the sine rule, but how would you find the angle θ or the length t in these two?

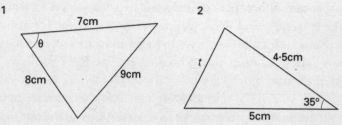

In triangle 1 you don't get any angles to start you off, and in triangle 2 you do get an angle of 35° but they don't give you the opposite side. You'll find the sine formula won't help! Instead you use the cosine rule which has two versions.

- To find an angle when you know all the sides (such as triangle 1):

$$\cos A = \frac{b^2 + c^2 - a^2}{2bc}$$

- To find the third side when you know the opposite angle (like triangle 2):

$$a^2 = b^2 + c^2 - 2bc \times \cos A$$

(Again, these formulae will be written out for you if you need them.)

Let's try them out with numbers. With triangle 1 we replace A with θ. Don't forget that *a* is the opposite side, and it doesn't

matter which way round you make the other sides into b and c.
We get: $\cos \theta = \frac{7^2 + 8^2 - 9^2}{2 \times 7 \times 8}$.

For triangle 2 we replace A with 35 and t is the opposite side so it replaces a in the formula: $t^2 = 5^2 + 4 \cdot 5^2 - (2 \times 5 \times 4 \cdot 5 \times \cos 35°)$.

Your turn. Work out these sums and see what you get for θ and t. Take it steadily and don't forget that to find θ you'll finish up using $\cos^{-1}$. It's also very easy to forget that the second formula starts with t^2 so once you've worked out the RHS you have to take the square root to get t.

Before you check your answers, take a few seconds to draw a rough diagram of each triangle. Do your answers *look* about right? (Answers on page 312.)

I: Area of a triangle (the sine formula)
We'll be having a better look at calculating areas on page 225, but as this section is all about trig it's a good place to see another little trick you can do with sines:

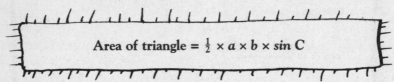

Area of triangle $= \frac{1}{2} \times a \times b \times sin$ **C**

For this formula you need to know the lengths of two sides and the angle between them.

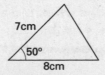

7cm

50°

8cm

In this case you would get: Area $= \frac{1}{2} \times 8 \times 7 \times \sin 50° = \frac{1}{2} \times 8 \times 7 \times 0 \cdot 766 = 21 \cdot 45 \text{ cm}^2$.

Bearings (north, south, east and west)

I: The sine rule and/or cosine rule are certain to come up somewhere, usually in a question about "bearings".

Suppose you're lost in a desert, clutching a mobile phone and you urgently need to reach the ice cream bar which is 50 km away. You could phone them and they might give directions such as "head towards the south-east and we're somewhere down there". It's a bit vague isn't it, especially when your tongue is starting to feel like an old doormat. After you've staggered 70 km towards the SE and missed it, you wish you'd known *exactly* which way to go. In fact, what you really needed was a precise compass bearing. So here's how it works:

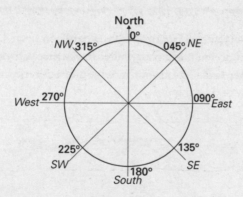

You'll see that the four normal points of a compass are put on a circle which has 360 degrees marked around it in a clockwise direction.

- If you travel north, you are going on a bearing of 0°
- South is 180°
- East is 090°
- West is 270°

You should also be aware of what the NE, SE, SW and NW bearings are. You'll notice that bearings are always given as 3 digits, so north-east is 045°.

If you are one of those people who can never remember which is east and which is west, think of a clock and say this out loud: "the number threeeeee is the same direction as eeeeeast".

(There was once a bloke on an American quiz show who had answered tons of tough questions and was finally going for $1,000,000 – but he missed out because he got east and west the wrong way round. True story!)

So there you are, 70 km away from where you started. Suppose you realized that you'd left your wallet back there. Obviously you need to stagger back 70 km, but in which direction?

It helps to do a rough drawing, so mark your starting position, and put a line through it pointing north. South-east is a bearing of 135° so measure this angle and draw a line to represent 70 km. You can then mark your finish position, and put in another line pointing north which is parallel to the first one. (Putting north pointers in is very quick if you do these drawings on squared paper.)

To get your bearing you need to know the angle we've marked here as θ and that's easy enough. If you look back at the angles section on page 164 you'll see that the 135° angle and θ together make 180°. Therefore θ = 45°. As the bearing is always measured going clockwise round from the north and there are 360° in a whole circle, we can see that the bearing for the return trip R° is: R = 360 – 45 = 315°.

There's a short cut to this. If you go somewhere, then want to come straight back, you need to turn round 180°. In terms of maths you can either add or subtract 180° to get the return bearing. So if you set off on a bearing of 135°, to get back you have to go at (135 + 180)° = 315°. Likewise, if you had set off on a bearing of 214°, to get back you would travel on a bearing of (214 – 180)° = 34°. This becomes obvious when you look back at the compass bearings diagram.

We'll now leave the desert for a while to visit a treasure island. The treasure map you found in a long–abandoned crisp packet says start at the palm tree, walk 3 km south and then 4 km east. Unfortunately, Black-hearted Jack has the same map and has already set off on his way south. You could cut him off by going straight to the treasure but what direction would you have to go in and how far away is it?

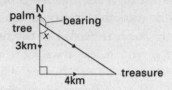

Hooray, it's a right-angled triangle, which makes life easy.

So $\tan x = \frac{4}{3}$. Which makes $x = 53.1°$.

Now we know x, we can take x away from $180°$ to find the bearing you have to go on to reach the treasure, which is $126.9°$. As it's a right-angled triangle, Pythagoras' theorem tell us that the square of the distance $= 3^2 + 4^2 = 9 + 16 = 25$. So the distance to the treasure $= \sqrt{25} = 5$ km.

H: Meanwhile in the desert you realize that you didn't leave your wallet after all so you don't need to go back. The trouble is there's no sign of the ice cream parlour so you give them another ring.

They tell you that you *should* have travelled 50 km on a bearing of 141°. As the vultures start circling you'll be wondering which direction to crawl in now, and how far will it be?

Again you need to mark the details out on a rough picture:

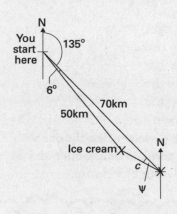

As well as marking the 70 km on a bearing of 135°, you mark 50 km on a bearing of 141° to show the journey you should have made. You can see the difference between the two bearings is 6° (which is exaggerated for this picture). Now you can draw in a line representing the journey from your finishing place to the ice cream parlour and let's see what we can work out:

- We can work out the distance c from the cosine rule: $c^2 = 50^2 + 70^2 - 2 \times 50 \times 70 \times \cos 6°$
- We can work out the angle marked as ψ because once we know what c is, we can use the sine rule to write: $\frac{\sin \psi}{50} = \frac{\sin 6°}{c}$ which becomes $\sin \psi = 50 \times \frac{\sin 6°}{c}$
- Once we know ψ we can work out the bearing we need. Look at the diagram:

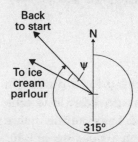

We've already worked out that to head back in the same direction is a bearing of 315° so the bearing to the ice-cream parlour is $(315 - \psi)°$.

That's it all set up for you, so now it's your turn to find the distance c and the bearing you need to reach the ice cream parlour. (Answers on page 312.)

At last you are perched on a stool with knickerbocker glory dripping off your face, and you can't help wondering how close you came to the ice cream parlour during your first 70 km walk.

If you draw the shortest line s from the ice cream parlour to your original path, you'll see it meets your path at a right angle. This splits the diagram up into two cute little right-angled triangles. One has c as the hypotenuse and ψ is one of the angles. The other has 50 km as the hypotenuse and an angle of 6°. It doesn't

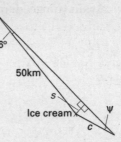

matter which one we use to find s but it's safer to use the one with 50 km and 6° in case we've made a mistake working out c and ψ. In that triangle $\frac{s}{50}$ = sin 6° so s = 50 × sin 6° = 5·23m.

TOP TIP
When you write out answers to "real" problems like this, don't just put s = [brilliantly worked out figure] km. Take a few seconds to fully write, "The closest I came to the ice cream parlour was [brilliantly worked out figure] km." It adds style, it makes more sense and might even be worth an extra mark or two.

H: Here's another "bearings" problem:

> **Two lifeboats A and B are searching for a dinghy in the fog. The lifeboats are 14 km apart and B is on a bearing of 145° from A. The dinghy sends out a distress signal which B detects on a bearing of 030°**

and A detects on a bearing of 105°. How far is the dinghy from each boat?

First do a rough diagram. It should look something like this:

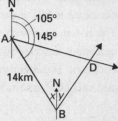

This information gives us a triangle with corners ABD. So let's work out the angles:

Angle BÂD : The bearing from A to B is 145° and the bearing to D is 105°, so it's plain to see that this angle is $(145 - 105)° = 40°$.

Angle DB̂A : The bearing from B to A is the reverse of A to B so it's $(145 + 180)° = 325°$. This makes the angle x in the diagram $= (360 - 325)° = 35°$. We were told that the bearing from B to D is 030° which is y in the diagram. The angle DB̂A $= x + y = 65°$.

Angle AD̂B : To complete the triangle, AD̂B $= 180 - 40 - 65 = 75°$.

For clarity you might want to draw out a second triangle with the angles you've just worked out:

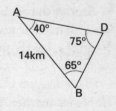

Now it's your turn. See if you can work out how far the dinghy is from A and from B. (Answers on page 312.)

Sin, cos and tan for angles over 90°

H: If you know the value of sin for any angle between 0° and 90°, you can get sin for any angle in a circle. This is because for each positive value of a sin there are two angles, and there are two more angles for each negative value of a sin. Try getting values out of your calculator for sin 15°, sin 165°, sin 195° and sin 345°. You'll see they are all the same number, but the last two are negative. Try the same experiment on your calculator with cos and tan. You'll notice that cos 165° and cos 195° are negative, and tan 165° and tan 345° are negative.

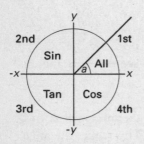

There's a little diagram that shows when values will be positive or negative. The axes on this graph divide it into four bits known as the 1st, 2nd 3rd and 4th quadrant. Look at the angle a which is always measured from the x axis. While a is less than 90°, the line is in the 1st quadrant which is marked "All". This means that all values of sin a, cos a and tan a are positive.

If the angle a is between 90° and 180° then the line will have moved round to the second quadrant. This is marked "Sin" which means that only the value for sin a will be positive. The others will be negative. (That's why sin 165° was positive but cos 165° and tan 165° were negative.)

In the third quadrant, the angle a is between 180° and 270° and "Tan" indicates only tan a will be positive.

In the fourth quadrant the angle a is between 270° and 360° and here "Cos" indicates only cos a will be positive.

This diagram is called the CAST diagram, which makes it easy to remember which order the letters come in.

H: Graphs of sin, cos and tan

A really good way of understanding how sin, cos and tan vary is to plot graphs of their values against degrees:

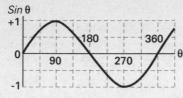

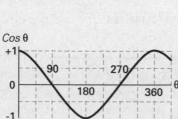

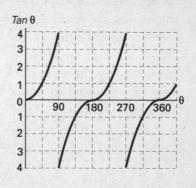

All these graphs repeat themselves every 360°.

Cos is exactly the same as sin but moved 90° along. (In fact sin $(\theta + 90) = \cos \theta$). The tan graph looks odd because it shoots off to infinity, then returns from minus infinity. Try asking your calculator what tan 90° is. You won't get much sense out of it, but if you try tan 89° and then tan 91° you'll start to understand why.

The usual sort of question you'll get in an exam involves plotting a graph, so let's see one:

> **Plot the graph of sin 2x for values 0° ≤ x ≤ 180°. Use it to solve the equation sin 2x = – 0·5.**

First we plot $y = \sin 2x$, so we need a table. . .

x =	0	20	40	60	80	100	120	140	160	180
$2x$ =	0	40	80	120	160	200	240	280	320	360
$y = \sin 2x =$	0	0·64	0·98	0·87	0·34	– 0·34	– 0·87	– 0·98	– 0·64	0·0

As the line will be the same shape as the usual sine curve, you just need enough points to see how it fits on the axis.

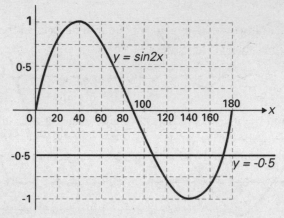

Here's the $y = \sin 2x$ line, and $y = -0.5$ has also been drawn in. All you do is see where the lines cross and bingo . . . you get $x = 105°$ and $165°$.

That wasn't too bad was it? This kind of question looks awful, but if you keep a cool head it's a dead cert for a few marks.

Transformations

This is rather a nice exam subject as it just involves drawing a few simple shapes on graph paper and then making them move and reflect across the page. It's certainly more fun than French verbs!

What? Even the irregular ones?

I: Reflections

Reflecting a shape in a line has the same effect as reflecting the shape in a mirror placed along the line. The image you get is reversed as it would be in a mirror and is as far behind the line as the original shape is in front of it.

TOP TIP
To find the image of a shape, find the images of the corners of the shape and join them up. If the shape is easy to draw, you may only need to find the images of some of the corners.

To find the image of any point in a line, draw a perpendicular line from the point to the line. Extend that on the other side of the line and mark the image point the same distance from the line.

Let's have a look at one:

Join the points P (2,1) Q (4,1) and R (4,4) to make a triangle. Reflect the triangle in the line $x = 1$ labelling it ('). Then reflect the new triangle in the line $y = x$ labelling it (").

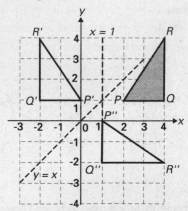

If you'd just been given the triangles PQR and P′Q′R′ and asked to find the line of reflection, you'd have to reverse the process. Draw lines joining each corner to its image then find the midpoint (e.g. join R to R' then mark the centre, and then do the same for P and P' and also Q and Q'). Finally join up these midpoints and this is the line of reflection.

I: Rotations

To help you think about rotation, imagine the shape is drawn on clear plastic and the plastic is fixed with a drawing pin at the centre of rotation. As you turn the plastic, the shape on it will turn as well.

To rotate a point, draw a line joining it to the centre of rotation. Draw a new line from the centre so the angle between the two lines is the angle of rotation. (Make sure you are going in the right direction.) Now mark the image point on the new line so it is the same distance from the centre as the new point. E.g. if you rotated point Z (1,3) 90° clockwise around point R (2,1) to Z′ you'd get this:

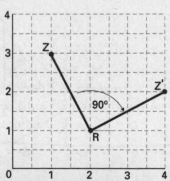

Notice that the lengths ZR and Z′R are the same and the angle between the lines is 90°.

> **TOP TIP**
> A set square is useful for drawing and checking reflections and rotations!

Now try this one yourself:

> Plot the points A (– 2,2), B (– 3,3), C (2,3) and D (1,2) to form a trapezium. Rotate this shape 90° clockwise around point (2,1) to create a second trapezium A′B′C′D′. Rotate ABCD 180° around (3·5,2) to create a third trapezium A″B″C″D″.

Answers on page 312.

Direction of rotation
Usually you will be told clockwise or anticlockwise. However, you should know that:

- rotating through + 90° is *anticlockwise*
- rotating through – 90° is *clockwise*.
- rotating a shape by 180° gives the same result clockwise or anticlockwise so usually people don't bother putting the direction in. Rotating by 180° is the same as using a scale factor of – 1 as you'll see in a minute.

Finding centres of rotations
If you are given a shape and its rotated position, you can work backwards and find the centre of rotation, the direction and the

angle involved. Just to beef things up a bit, we'll use more complicated numbers for this one but as long as you plot your points and measure carefully, it isn't any harder.

What is the translation between triangles P (6,2) Q (7·5,2) R (7·7,– 0·3) and P′ (2·5,2·6) Q′ (2,4) R′ (4,5)?

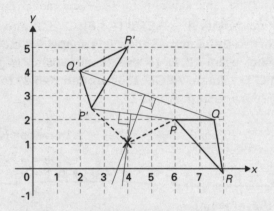

The question doesn't tell you it's a rotation but you can see it is by looking at the diagram. First you need to find the centre of rotation. Join a pair of corresponding points such as P and P′ then do a perpendicular bisection on the line. (This is the same as the locus of points equidistant from P and P′. Look back at page 172 to see how to do this.) You then join another pair of corresponding points such as Q and Q′ and bisect that line too. Where the bisectors meet is the centre of rotation. In this example the lines meet at (4,1).

Next you need the angle of rotation so draw lines from two of the corresponding points to the centre and see what the angle is between them. Here the dotted lines join P and P′ to the centre, and when you measure the angle you get 110°.

The direction of rotation is easy – in this case you can see it's

(+ 110°) or if you prefer: 110° anticlockwise from P to P'. NOTE: You could go the "long way round" and say the angle of rotation is (− 250°) or 250° clockwise.

If they ask for the inverse of the translation, all they need to know is what would you do to put P'Q'R' back on to PQR. Simple, you just rotate P'Q'R' in the opposite direction. The inverse has the same centre point (4,1) and moves through an angle of (− 110°) or 110° clockwise.

As a bit of practice, go back to our first question on rotations. Draw a fresh diagram to find the centre and angle of rotation for transforming A'B'C'D' into A"B"C"D". (Answers on page 312.)

Sometimes you might be asked to do more than one operation on a shape, for instance a rotation followed by a reflection. Just follow the instructions they give you, and make sure you do the operations in the right order!

Yes, I always forget that!

I: Enlargements and reductions with scale factors

An enlargement produces an image which is the same shape as the original but a different size. A scale factor larger than 1 or smaller than − 1 makes the image larger. A scale factor between − 1 and + 1 makes the image smaller. If the scale factor is positive, the object and the image are the same side of the centre of enlargement but if it is negative they are on opposite sides.

To find the image of a point after an enlargement, draw a line joining the point to the centre of enlargement and measure it. Multiply that length by the scale factor to find the distance of the image point from the centre. If the answer is positive, measure that distance along the line in the same direction as the original point. If the answer is negative, measure the distance in the opposite direction.

Look at this one:

Draw a triangle with vertices L (– 2,1) M (– 2,3) N (– 1,1).
- **From the point (– 4,1) enlarge LMN by a scale factor of + 3 to produce L'M'N'.**
- **Through the point (– 2,0) transform LMN by a scale factor of – 1 to produce L"M"N".**
- **Through the point (4,0) transform L'M'N' by a scale factor of – $\frac{1}{2}$ to produce L'''M'''N'''.**

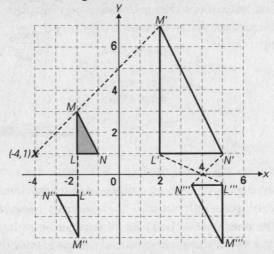

The original LMN is shaded. Each new point on L'M'N' is 3 times further from the point (– 4,1) than LMN in a straight line. (The dotted line joining (– 4,1) M and M' has been drawn in to show this. The distance between (− 4,1) and M′ is three times the distance between (− 4,1) and M.) Both triangles are on the same side of the point (− 4,1) because the scale factor is positive.

With L″M″N″ each point is the same distance from (− 2,0) as LMN, but *on the other side* because the scale factor was negative. Notice that multiplying by a scale factor of − 1 through (− 2,0) is the same as rotating by 180° around (− 2,0). If the scale factor had been + 1, then the new triangle would be sitting exactly on top of the original.

Finding a scale factor

> Plot (− 5,0) (− 5,4) (− 1,4) (− 4,3) and join them to make an arrowhead. Plot (2,1) (4,1) (4,3) (3·5,1·5) to make a second arrowhead. Find the point of transformation of these two shapes and the scaling factor between the first and second shape.

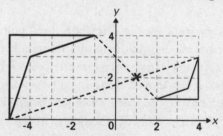

Once you've plotted the shapes, all you need to do is join up some of the corresponding points, as these dotted lines show you. Where the lines cross is the centre of enlargement − in this case (1,2) − and by measuring how far each shape is from this point you get the scaling factor. The second shape is only half the distance from the point as the first shape, and it is on the opposite side of the point, so the scaling factor is − $\frac{1}{2}$.

For a bit of practice, look back at the diagram on page 214. Draw out a fresh diagram to help you find the point of transformation and scaling factor that would convert L'M'N' into L"M"N". (Answers on page 312.)

I: Translations with column vectors

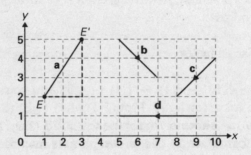

Column vectors are a way of describing how points, lines and shapes are moved about, and the results are usually drawn out on squared or graph paper. In the diagram the point E has moved to E' and the line it has moved along is called a vector. You could write this vector as $\vec{EE'}$ but here we've just labelled it **a**. You can see that **a** involves a movement of 2 squares in the x direction and 3 squares in the y direction. This is written down as a **column vector**. **a** = $\binom{x}{y}$ where x and y are how far you move in each direction. Here you can see that **a** = $\binom{2}{3}$.

If you were to move from E' back to E, this would be called the **inverse vector** and you could write this as − **a** (or $\vec{E'E}$). You can convert a column vector to its inverse by multiplying both numbers by − 1 so − **a** = $\binom{-2}{-3}$.

Understand it so far? Just make sure by checking what the

column vectors are for **b**, **c** and **d**. What is the inverse of **d**? (Answers on page 312.)

Don't get column vectors confused with fractions! *You can't cancel through.*

If you are told to draw a vector on squared or graph paper, it doesn't matter where you start, so long as you move the correct number of squares horizontally and vertically. Now let's see the usual sort of question:

> Draw the triangle T (– 1,– 1) U (2,3) V (2,1). Translate it to T′U′V′ with the vector ($\frac{5}{2}$). Translate the new image to T″U″V″ with the vector (_$\frac{2}{4}$).

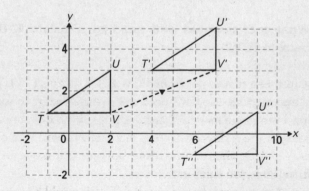

First look at how point V has moved to point V′. Point V is at (2,1) which is the quick way of writing the position $x = 2$ and $y = 1$. When you move V using the vector ($\frac{5}{2}$) this means you move it 5 places in the x direction and 2 places in the y direction. This means the new x co-ordinate is $(2 + 5)$ and the new y co-ordinate is $(1 + 2)$. You end up with V′ at $(7,3)$. The dotted line shows the direction and magnitude of this vector, and you can write this as: $\vec{VV'} = \binom{5}{2}$. In the same way the positions of T and U have been moved by the vector $\binom{5}{2}$ to their new positions at T′ and U′.

When the triangle T′U′V′ is translated to T″U″V″, you'll see each point has been moved by the vector $\binom{2}{-4}$. If you check the co-ordinates of each point before and after the move, you'll see the x co-ordinate has changed by $+ 2$ and the y co-ordinate has changed by $- 4$.

Suppose you had to translate triangle TUV directly to T″U″V″. What would the vector be?

There are two ways to do this. One way is to add the two vectors we've already used together. You get: $\binom{5}{2} + \binom{2}{-4} = \binom{5+2}{2-4} = \binom{7}{-2}$. Alternatively you can look at a pair of points like T and T″ and see how they have changed.

What vector would you need to translate T″U″V″ back to TUV?

We've just seen that to get from TUV to T″U″V″ it's $\binom{7}{-2}$. To go in the opposite direction we need the inverse vector so we just multiply both numbers by $- 1$ and get $\binom{-7}{2}$.

I: Adding column vectors
As we've just seen, if you need to add column vectors, you just add the top bits together and then add the bottom bits together.

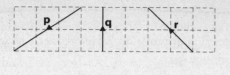

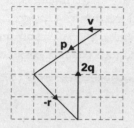

Here we've got three vectors: $\mathbf{p} = \begin{pmatrix} -3 \\ -2 \end{pmatrix}$ $\mathbf{q} = \begin{pmatrix} 0 \\ 2 \end{pmatrix}$ $\mathbf{r} = \begin{pmatrix} -2 \\ 2 \end{pmatrix}$

What would $\mathbf{p} - \mathbf{r} + 2\mathbf{q}$ be as a single column vector?

Easy: $\begin{pmatrix} -3 - (-2) + 0 \\ -2 - 2 + 4 \end{pmatrix} = \begin{pmatrix} -1 \\ 0 \end{pmatrix}$

You can check an answer like this by drawing a little diagram. Here you can see the answer to this sum is marked as vector $\mathbf{v}$.

Here are some for you to work out:

Describe the following as single column vectors:
a) $2\mathbf{r} + \mathbf{q} + \mathbf{p}$ b) $\mathbf{q} - 3\mathbf{p} - \mathbf{r}$ c) $2\mathbf{p} - 3\mathbf{r} + 5\mathbf{q}$

Answers on page 313.

I: Moving shapes around a grid
Have a go at at this question as a recap. Remember that:

- Vectors simply move an image without changing it in any other way.
- Rotation turns the image round.
- Reflection produces a mirror image.
- Scale factors change the size of an image and negative scale factors also turn the image round 180°.

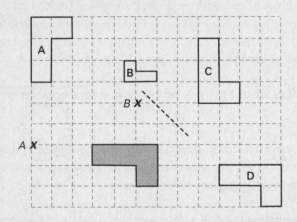

In the diagram the shaded shape has undergone four different operations to produce the images A, B, C and D. Can you describe each one?

Answers on page 313.

TOP TIP

Remember: Apart from scale factors, all these transformation operations produce images that are congruent with the original.

I: Double reflections

If you reflect a figure once you get an inverted (or mirror) image. If you reflect it twice in the same line the image goes back to the original. If you use different mirror lines for each reflection you get some interesting results.

Thankfully, this type of mirror never comes up in GCSE.

Two parallel mirror lines = translation

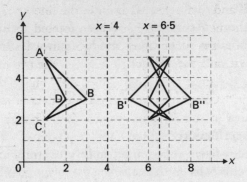

The arrowhead ABCD has been reflected in the line $x = 4$ and again in the line $x = 6 \cdot 5$. (Notice that a mirror line can cut inside the shape – you have to draw the results carefully! Only points B′ and B″ have been labelled for clarity.) The final image A″B″C″D″ is a translation of the original ABCD – in other words ABCD has just moved along a bit. Can you see what the translation is? (Answer on page 313.)

Two skew mirror lines = rotation

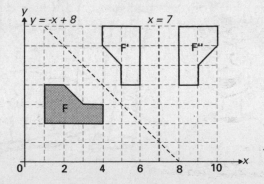

Here the shaded figure F has been reflected in the line $y = -x + 8$ to give F′ and then reflected again in the line $x = 7$ to give F″. This is the same result as if F had been rotated about the point (7,1) which is the point where the two mirror lines cross. The angle of rotation is *twice* the angle between the two mirror lines. In this case the angle between the lines is 45° and so the angle of rotation is 90°. Clearly this is in a clockwise direction, so it's − 90°.

Look back at the diagram on page 209. Triangle PQR was reflected twice through two skew lines to produce P″Q″R″, so this is the same as a single rotation. What is the centre of rotation and the angle? (Answers on page 313.)

Measurement

F: These days we have the metric system and if you knew how miserable everyday sums used to be without it, you'd grab an atlas and kiss the map of France because that's where it was invented. How would you fancy having to multiply by 1760 all the time or divide by 112? And those were the days before calculators!

The metric system starts by having all measurements of length based on the **metre** (m). (The French worked out that 1 m was one ten millionth of the distance from the North Pole to the equator on a line passing through Paris!)

Trés clever, n'est-ce pas?

All masses are based on the **gram** (g) and all "capacities" are based on the **litre** (l). These three basic units of measurement are all linked together by the fact that 1 litre of water has a mass of 1,000 g and it will fit in a cube measuring 0·1 m × 0·1 m × 0·1 m.

Metres, grams and litres can be made more convenient to use by adding words in front:

- **kilo** = 1,000 or 10^3, so 1 kg = 1,000 g
- **centi** = 0·01 or $\frac{1}{100}$ or 10^{-2}, so 100 cm = 1 m
- **milli** = 0·001 or $\frac{1}{1000}$ or 10^{-3}, so 1000 ml = 1 l

It's useful to remember that 1 cm^3 and 1 ml are the same size, so 1 litre = 1,000 cm^3. (There are several other words that are not so common including **mega** = 1,000,000 or 10^6 and **micro** = 0·000001 or 10^{-6} or one millionth.)

- **1 tonne** or **1 T** = 1000 kg
- **1 cubic metre** or **1 m^3** = 1000 l

(If you have 1000 l of water, it would occupy a cube measuring 1 m × 1 m × 1 m, so large capacity measurements tend to be in cubic metres rather than litres. Incidentally, 1 m^3 of water has a mass of 1 T.)

Imperial units
Some old-fashioned units still turn up occasionally and in the USA they're still what *everyone* uses *all the time*. Here are the main ones with their approximate metric equivalents.

Length   12 inches = 1 foot; 3 feet = 1 yard; 1760 yards = 1 mile
              1 foot ≈ 30 cm; 1 yard ≈ 0·9 m; 1 mile ≈ 1·6 km
Weight   16 ounces = 1 pound (lb); 14 pounds = 1 stone;

2240 pounds = 1 ton
1 lb ≈ 0·45 kg (and the easy one. . .) 1 ton ≈ 1 tonne

Capacity   8 pints = 1 gallon
1 pint ≈ 0·57 litres

TOP TIP
You may find it easier to remember 1 kg = 2·2 lbs and 1 litre = $1\frac{3}{4}$ pints.

F: Converting imperial and metric systems

If a recipe asks for 3·5 pints of vinegar, how many litres do you need?

As 1 pint ≈ 0·57 litres, 3·5 pints ≈ 3·5 × 0·57 = 1·995 litres. (Hint: Check this with your common sense. As litres are bigger than pints, your recipe will need *fewer* litres than pints. 1.995 is less than 3.5 so the answer looks OK.)

Try these yourself:

1. You're fixing an old wheelbarrow and it needs a 3-inch bolt. How long is this in metric units?

2. Your bike has been found 27 km away. How many miles and yards is that?

3. A car holds 11 gallons of petrol which costs £1.35 per litre. How much to fill it right up?

Answers on page 313.

225

F: Getting used to the size of units

You should have a reasonable idea of how big or heavy units are
and the way to do this is to think of a few things that you are
really familiar with. For example, you might be about 1·5 m tall,
so if you are asked how high a room is, estimate how many clones
of yourself you'd need to stand on each other's heads to reach the
ceiling. It's also handy to know these details in imperial units – if
you're 1·5 m high, that's about 5 feet.

Here are a few more *approximate* guides. These are close
enough for estimations but not for calculations:

	metric	imperial
1 pint or $\frac{1}{2}$ litre of milk	$\frac{1}{2}$ kg	1 lb
A bag of sugar	1 kg	2 lbs
A football's diameter	30 cm	1 foot
A two-storey house height	8 m	25 feet
A tall man of medium build:		
– height	1·8 m	6 feet
– weight	80 kg	170 lbs
The length of a football pitch	100 m	110 yards
The weight of a large bull	1 T	1 ton
London to Edinburgh	400 miles	650 km

Length, area and volume

F: Suppose you are building a box out of card and tape. You could start by cutting out a shape in the card like this (all measurements in cm):

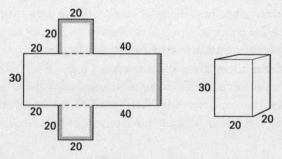

Three different sorts of measurement arise here.

Length: What length of tape do you need? This only requires a measurement in *one* dimension or 1-D. The diagram has shaded lines to show where the tape needs to go. If you add up the lengths of all these lines you find that you need (6 × 20) + (1 × 30) cm = 150 cm of tape.

Area: How much card are you actually using in making the box? The diagram is divided into three areas: the main sides and the top and bottom. Each area needs to be calculated from measurements in *two* dimensions or 2-D which we'll call height and width. The area making the four main sides is 30 cm high and 80 cm wide. As this is a rectangle, you get the total area by multiplying these together to get 30 × 80 = 2400 cm². The top and bottom both measure 20 cm × 20 cm, so each measures 400 cm². Adding all three areas gives 2400 + 400 + 400 = 3200 cm². The units are in cm² because they arose from multiplying cm × cm and anything multiplied by itself is squared.

Volume: How much does the box hold? This requires measurements in 3-D: height, width and depth. As this is a cuboid we multiply them together to get a volume of $30 \times 20 \times 20 = 12{,}000 \text{ cm}^3$. Notice the units are in cm^3.

F: Perimeters and areas of different shapes

A perimeter is the line round the edge of a shape such as a fence around a field or a border round a picture.

There are no short cuts, you've GOT to know all these formulae. Study the pictures and get them in your head:

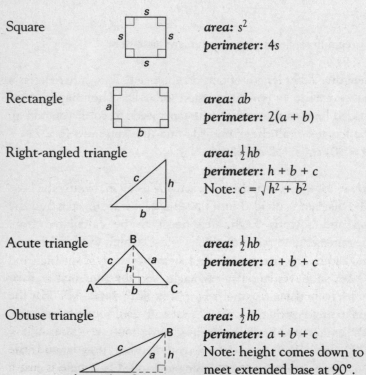

Square

area: s^2
perimeter: $4s$

Rectangle

area: ab
perimeter: $2(a + b)$

Right-angled triangle

area: $\frac{1}{2}hb$
perimeter: $h + b + c$
Note: $c = \sqrt{h^2 + b^2}$

Acute triangle

area: $\frac{1}{2}hb$
perimeter: $a + b + c$

Obtuse triangle

area: $\frac{1}{2}hb$
perimeter: $a + b + c$
Note: height comes down to meet extended base at 90°.

Parallelogram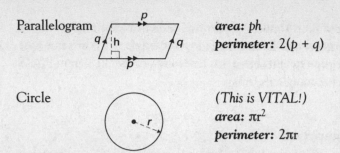
area: ph
perimeter: $2(p + q)$

Circle
(*This is VITAL!*)
area: πr^2
perimeter: $2\pi r$

The only formula that might turn up which you don't have to remember is:

Trapezium
area: $\frac{1}{2}(d + c)h$
perimeter: $c + d + e + f$

If you're doing the intermediate or higher level, you should know the "sin" formula for area of a triangle: $\frac{1}{2}bc \sin A$ (see page 198).

When areas are the same

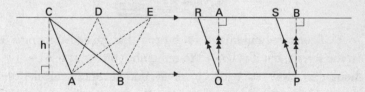

If triangles have the same base length and the same height, their areas are the same. So area ABC = area ABD = area ABE. (By the way, triangles are a bit of a pain because even if you know all three sides you have to work out the height or know one of the angles.)

If parallelograms have the same base length and the same height, their areas are the same. As a rectangle is just a parallelogram with 90° corners, this rather helpfully means that a parallelogram has the same area as a rectangle with the same base and the same height. Here you'll see area of parallelogram PQRS = area of rectangle PQAB.

F: π and circles

π (called "pi") is a symbol representing 3·1415926 . . . which is a number that goes on for ever and many millions of slightly pointless computer hours have been spent trying to get to the end of it without success.

Your calculator should have a π button that immediately puts it on the screen, but if you need to remember it then π = 3·14 or $\frac{22}{7}$ should be close enough. However, for accurate calculations always use the π button on your calculator or you might get the wrong answer and lose marks.

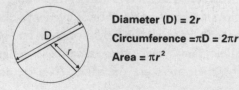

Diameter (D) = 2r

Circumference = πD = 2πr

Area = πr^2

π is the exact ratio of the circumference (or perimeter) of a circle to its diameter. It also allows us to find the area with the formula: area = πr^2.

Just for practice:

1. Circle E has a radius of 12 cm. What is its area and its perimeter?

2. Circle F has an area of 120 mm^2. What is its diameter?

3. Crop circle G has a perimeter of 800 m. If the whole circle has been completely flattened, what area of corn has been ruined by some anorak with a garden roller pretending to be a UFO?

Give all these answers in the appropriate units to 2 d.p.

Answers on page 313.

F: Volumes

In the foundation exams they only ask you to deal with volumes of prisms. These are solids that have the same shape at the top and bottom and sides that go straight up, and include cuboids, cylinders and triangular prisms. Here's the general formula for them all:

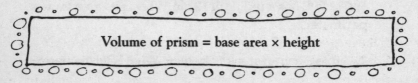

Volume of prism = base area × height

Cuboid 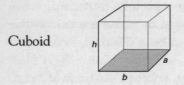 **volume:** abh

Cylinder **volume:** $\pi r^2 h$

radius = r

Triangular prism **volume:** triangle base area $\times h$

(In this diagram we have a right-angled triangle, so volume $= \frac{1}{2}abh$.)

Odd-shaped prism **volume:** Ah
(As long as you know the area of the base, the formula always works.)

Area = A

I: Surface areas of prisms

You usually work this out by splitting it into three bits: the top, the bottom and the sides. The top and bottom are easy enough: they are each equal to the base area. The area of all the other sides together = the base perimeter × the height.

For the cuboid, the base area = ab, so top and bottom together = $2ab$. The base perimeter = $2(a + b)$, so the area of the sides = $2(a + b)h$. This gives: surface area of cuboid = $2ab + 2(a + b)h = 2ab + 2ah + 2bh = 2(ab + ah + bh)$.

Of course, if you added up the areas of all six sides individually you would get the same answer.

> **Find the formulae for the surface area of the cylinder and right-angled triangular prism as shown in the diagram on page 232.**

Answers on page 314.

H: Extra formulae: pyramids, cones and spheres

Cones

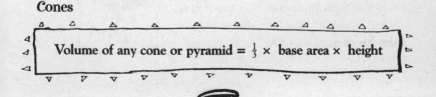

Volume of any cone or pyramid = $\frac{1}{3}$ × base area × height

233

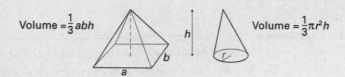

Volume $= \frac{1}{3}abh$ Volume $= \frac{1}{3}\pi r^2 h$

It doesn't matter if the cone or pyramid is sticking straight upwards or slanting over, as long as you know the base area and the height perpendicular to the base, then you can work out the volume.

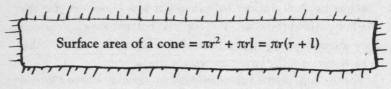

Surface area of a cone $= \pi r^2 + \pi rl = \pi r(r + l)$

r is the radius and l is the length of the sloping side.

It's probably more use to remember this formula in two bits because: πr^2 = base area and πrl = area of the sloping sides. (This is rather a neat result for something that could have been complicated, don't you think?)

If you get a question about making funnels out of cardboard, this involves an open cone, so you only need the sloping side area. Notice that l is NOT the perpendicular height, but thanks to Pythagoras the height h, l and r are all linked by $r^2 + h^2 = l^2$. (This is the sort of knowledge that if you suddenly produce it at the right moment, examiners leap round thinking they've discovered a new Einstein.)

Spheres

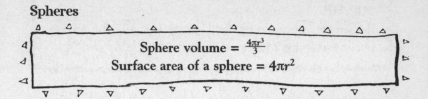

$$\text{Sphere volume} = \frac{4\pi r^3}{3}$$
$$\text{Surface area of a sphere} = 4\pi r^2$$

What happens if you chop a sphere in half to get a hemisphere? You only have half the curved area you started with (so that's $2\pi r^2$), but of course a flat circle has appeared where you chopped it and this has area πr^2. Add these together and get:

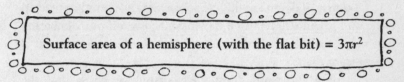

Surface area of a hemisphere (with the flat bit) = $3\pi r^2$

I: How length, area and volume units compare

For linear measurements 1 m = 100 cm = 1000 mm. But look at what happens with an area of 1 m^2 (sometimes written 1 sq m): 1 m^2 = (100 cm)^2 = 10,000 cm^2; and also 1 m^2 = (1000 mm)^2 = 1,000,000 mm^2.

And in the same way for volume: 1 m^3 = 1,000,000 cm^3 = 1,000,000,000 mm^3.

> **If a dose of vaccine is $\frac{1}{2}$ ml, how many people can a doctor treat with a tank containing 4·7 m^3?**

Sort out the units first. 1 ml and 1 cm^3 are the same size, so $\frac{1}{2}$ ml = 0·5 cm^3.

So the question becomes how many 0.5 cm^3 are there in 4·7 m^3?

We've just seen there are 1,000,000 cm^3 in 1 m^3, so the doctor has 4,700,000 cm^3 of vaccine. The answer is therefore 4,700,000 ÷ 0·5 = 9,400,000. So the doctor can treat 9,400,000 people!

Sometimes it isn't obvious whether you're dealing with 1, 2, or 3 dimensions. Suppose a wall is 3·6 m^2 and you need 2·5 litres of paint to cover it – the area of the wall is 2-D , but "litres" are a volume measurement in 3-D. How does this volume of paint become an area?

Of course, it doesn't really, because when the paint is spread on the wall it will still be three-dimensional, even if one dimension is very small! Let's work out what this dimension is to 3 significant digits.

Providing the paint doesn't evaporate, we know that the volume of paint will be 2·5 litres whatever shape it occupies. When the paint is on the wall it will be in the shape of a prism with a base area of 3·6 m^2 and a thickness t. This means the volume will be 3·6t m^3, so 2·5 litres = 3·6t m^3.

In this sum we'll be working out the thickness in metres, even though we know it will be tiny! We also need to convert the 2·5 litres of paint to m^3. As there are 1000 litres/m^3 we have 0·0025 m^3 of paint. We get: 3·6t = 0·0025; so t = 0·0025 ÷ 3·6 = 0·000694 m. You could give the answer like this, or put t = 6·94 × 10^{-4} m or 0·694 mm.

I: How to tell lengths, areas and volumes apart

Lengths only have one dimension, so any formula involving lengths is linear such as: the perimeter of a rectangle = $2(a + b)$. Note the a and b are *added*. You will NOT get two or more measurements multiplied together.

Areas have two dimensions, so any area formula will either have two measurements multiplied together or one measurement squared. So: the area of a rectangle = ab; the area of a circle = πr^2.

Volumes have three dimensions, so any volume formula will have three measurements multiplied together, whether they are the same or all different. So: the volume of a cuboid = abc; the volume of a cylinder = $\pi r^2 h$.

If you are given a formula and can't remember what it's for, see how many measurements are multiplied together. If you were given the formula $\frac{1}{2}(a + 2b)h$ and were told that a, b and h were all in cm, then even if you hadn't a clue what shape or lump it was describing, you would still know that this is an area formula because when you expand the expression each term has two measurements multiplied together.

H: Similar areas and volumes

Let's say you have one little sugar cube measuring 1 cm along each side. You decide to put some cubes together to make a bigger cube measuring 2 cm each side, and then – carried away by the excitement of it all – you make another even bigger cube measuring 3 cm each side.

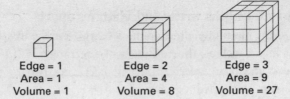

Edge = 1	Edge = 2	Edge = 3
Area = 1	Area = 4	Area = 9
Volume = 1	Volume = 8	Volume = 27

These three cubes are similar because they are all exactly the same shape. They are also in a fixed scale. The linear scales are 1:2:3 and any linear measurement you take on these cubes will be in those proportions. Suppose you decide to tie a little ribbon around each cube (gift-wrapping them for a loved one perhaps), the lengths of the ribbons will be in the proportions 1:2:3.

Thanks.
They're lovely!

Now suppose you decide to wallpaper each cube. The areas are 2-D so the proportions are squared resulting in the ratios $1^2:2^2:3^2$ which gives 1:4:9. You can see this from the diagram, by counting the squares on the side of each cube.

If you want to weigh each cube, you're dealing with the volumes and these are in cubic proportions which are $1^3:2^3:3^3$ giving 1:8:27. Again you can check this by counting the individual cubes in each cube.

> Squaring and cubing proportions works for any shape
> and even works in reverse.

You've blown a balloon up to a diameter of 59 cm. You decide to let exactly half the air out. What will the diameter reduce to?

The amount of air in a balloon is an indication of the volume, so if you let half of it out the volume will be $\frac{1}{2}$. In terms of proportion, the volume is the linear measurement cubed, so to find the how the diameter has changed we need the cube root of $\frac{1}{2}$, which we can write as $\sqrt[3]{0.5}$ or $(0.5)^{\frac{1}{3}}$. So the new diameter = 0·793 of the old diameter. The new diameter is $(0.5)^{\frac{1}{3}} \times$ old diameter = $(0.5)^{\frac{1}{3}} \times 59$ cm = 46·83 cm.

Angles, tangents and chords

H: At the higher level you're quite likely to be given a diagram with a circle and a few lines and you have to work out what the angles and measurements are. We've explained all the bits you need with as many pictures as we can without making this into a colouring book, so make sure you can see how the statements apply to each picture.

This all might seem rather a lot to remember, but once you get the hang of a few of them, the others become obvious. A few words to learn first:

Cyclic quadrilateral   A four-sided figure whose points all fit on the same circle. You can describe the points as **concyclic**.

239

Equidistant   "Equal distance from."

Subtended   If you have two points and draw a line
                    from each that meet at an angle, that
                    angle is "subtended" by the two points.
                    (In this circle, the angle x is subtended
                    from A and B. So is the angle y.)

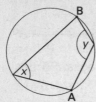

H: Tangent facts

A tangent always meets a radius at right angles.

**The two tangents drawn from an external point are
equal in length.**

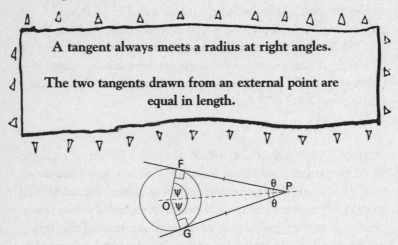

In the diagram, angles PGO and PFO both equal 90°, and the
lengths PG = PF. The diagram also shows that if you join the
centre of the circle to the external points, you get two congruent
right-angled triangles. You can see which sides and angles are
equal and these often give you the key to answering questions.

Suppose you were told angle FP̂G was 70°, what is the angle
PÔG ? Easy, because OP̂G = ½ FP̂G = 35°. Therefore to complete
the triangle PÔG has to be (180 − 90 − 35) = 55°.

As soon as right angles come into things, look out for Pythagoras' theorem. Try this one:

> **A tangent of length 24 cm is drawn from point P to touch a circle of diameter 14 cm. How far is P from the centre of the circle? (Hint: draw a diagram first!)**

Answers on page 314.

H: Angle-in-a-circle facts

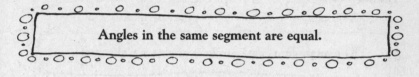

Angles in the same segment are equal.

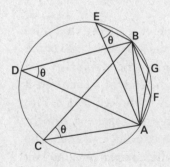

In the diagram, A and B are two points on a circle. (Quite often these points will be joined to make a **chord.**) Any angles subtended by AB at the circumference in the same segment of the circle will be equal, so angles $A\hat{C}B = A\hat{D}B = A\hat{E}B$. Also, in the other segment, $A\hat{F}B = A\hat{G}B$.

The angle at the centre is twice the angle at the circumference.

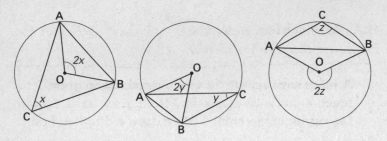

If you subtend an angle from AB to the centre and another angle to the far edge of the circle, AÔB = 2 AĈB. In the third drawing, just to be awkward the angle is subtended in the smaller segment of the circle. In this case the angle at the circumference (z) is half the size of the *reflex* angle at the centre ($2z$).

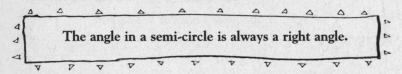

The angle in a semi-circle is always a right angle.

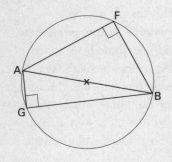

This is one of the most vital rules in maths and is a special case of the previous rule, where points A and B are on the ends of a diameter. If you join A to the centre and B to the centre, they make a straight line which is an angle of 180°. The angle at the circumference is half this value, so it doesn't matter where on the circle F and G are, both angles have to be 90°.

Quite often this is used the other way round. If you have *any* right-angled triangle, the centre point of the hypotenuse is equidistant from all three corners. So if you have a right-angled triangle and want to draw a circle that touches all the corners, the centre will be halfway along the hypotenuse.

H: Cyclic quadrilateral facts

Opposite angles of a cyclic quadrilateral add up to 180°.

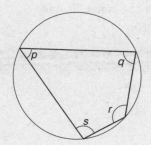

In this diagram: $p + r = 180°$ and $q + s = 180°$. It doesn't matter how odd a shape you try to make, this is always true!

The exterior angle of a cyclic quadrilateral is equal to the interior opposite angle.

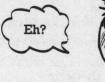

Eh?

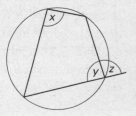

Don't be put off by this grand statement. As we've just seen, $x + y = 180°$ because they are opposite angles, and $y + z = 180°$ because they are on a straight line. So $x = z$. Super.

H: Chord facts

The shortest line joining the centre of the circle to a chord bisects the chord at 90°.

Chords of the same length are the same distance from the centre.

The diagram illustrates both facts. P is the mid-point of chord AB, so OP̂A and OP̂B are both right angles. The length OP is the distance of the chord from the centre.

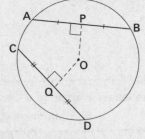

If OQ̂D is shown as 90°, then you know that Q is in the middle of CD. Also, if you know the lengths AB = CD then OQ = OP.

The same thing works backwards. If you know OQ = OP then that must means the chords AB and CD are the same length.

The angle and tangent and chord theorem

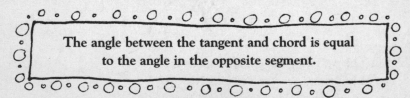

The angle between the tangent and chord is equal to the angle in the opposite segment.

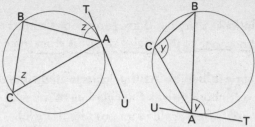

This seems confusing until you look at the pictures. In both diagrams BÂT is the angle between the chord AB and the tangent which touches the circle at A. AĈB is the angle in the opposite segment, in other words it's the angle subtended by AB on the other side of the circle from the angle BÂT . The theorem tells us that BÂT = AĈB. Incidentally, it doesn't matter where on the opposite side of the circle point C is, the angle AĈB will always be the same, because of the "angles in the same segment are equal" theorem. By the way, in both diagrams AB̂C = UÂC, but can you see why? (And don't just look straight at the answer on page 314!)

Now we know all these facts, it's time to see how they come up. Don't forget to look out for right angles, isosceles triangles and congruent triangles:

In the diagram below, AC and AB are tangents to the circle, COD is a straight line. If angle CÂB is 50°, can you work out every marked angle in the diagram and explain how you got the answer?

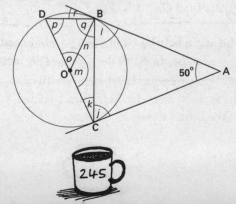

The diagram looks scary but don't panic. Start with the triangle where you know one of the angles and work from there.

In triangle ABC, AC = AB (tangents from the same point).
So $j + l = 180° - 50° = 130°$ (angle sum of triangle).
So $j = l = 65°$ (base angle of an isosceles triangle).
$k + j = 90°$ (tangent meeting radius).
So $k = 25°$.
In triangle OCB, OC = OB (radii).
So $n = k = 25°$.
So $m = 180° - 25° - 25° = 130°$ (angle sum of triangle).

Now you try to finish it off. Don't forget to put the explanations – the question has asked for them so you'll lose marks if you don't. (Answers on page 314.)

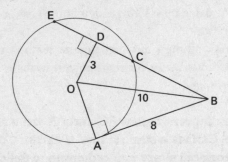

In the diagram above, AB is a tangent. With the given lengths find CE to 3 d.p.

First of all we need the radius of the circle, and with a bit of Pythagoras on triangle AOB we see that $OA^2 = 10^2 - 8^2$. A little bell might ring in your head here as this is a 3–4–5 triangle, although in this case the sides are doubled so it's a 6–8–10 triangle. You'll find OA = 6.

The sneaky bit is that you have to draw in OC. As this is another radius of the circle, it will also = 6. OCD is a right-angled triangle and again using Pythagoras you get $DC^2 = OC^2 - OD^2 = 36 - 9 = 27$. $DC = 5.196$. As point D comes in the middle of CE, the length $CE = 2 \times 5.196 = 10.392$.

Incidentally, if you use sine and cosine you could work out all the angles on this diagram too! Go on, it's good practice. . . (Answers on page 314.)

Don't push it...

More vectors

We've already seen how column vectors can translate shapes around a grid, but the higher level takes the whole idea of vectors a bit further.

H: Vectors and scalars

A plain positive or negative number is called a **scalar**. For example 3, 2001 and – 15 are all scalars because all we know about them is their **magnitude** which is a posh way of saying how big they are.

A vector is a bit more complicated because it describes a magnitude together with a direction. If you push the fridge a distance of 2 m into the middle of the kitchen, that's a vector because it has magnitude of 2 m and a direction. If a north wind blows your washing away at 20 mph, that's also a vector.

You can illustrate a vector by drawing a line with an arrowhead. The length of the line shows the magnitude of the vector, and the arrow shows which direction it is acting in.

H: Adding and subtracting vectors

If you tag a second arrowed line on to the first, this is like adding two vectors.

Suppose you've got a map for buried treasure which says to go 4 paces north-east then 3 paces east. You could describe your movements as two vectors:

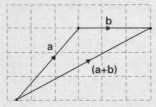

a is the 4 paces NE and **b** is the 3 paces E. If you wanted to describe the whole movement as one vector, it would be **(a + b)**. Combining vectors give you the **resultant vector** or just the "resultant".

Of course, you could have reached the same spot by first going 3 paces E and then 4 paces NE. This is the same as moving along vector **b** and then **a**. The actual path you follow will be different, but the finishing place is the same, and you can describe the direct vector to it as

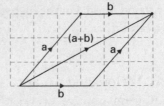

(b + a) which is clearly the same as **(a + b)**. You can see in the diagram that the two routes form a parallelogram, and so the rule for this is rather predictably called the parallelogram rule:

It doesn't matter in what order you add vectors.

Once you've found the treasure, you'll want to get straight back to the start point. To go in the opposite direction, you need the inverse of the resultant vector, which just means changing the signs.

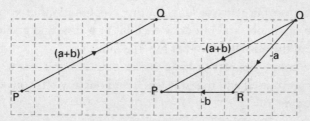

The direct way to the treasure was **(a + b)** so the direct way back is **– (a + b)**. As the diagram shows, this is the same as going along **– a** and then **– b**. So **– (a + b) = – a – b.**

Remember that you can also write vectors as pairs of capital letters. In the diagram **(a + b)** is the same as $\overrightarrow{PQ}$. There are loads of ways of writing the inverse vector: **– (a + b)** $= -\overrightarrow{PQ} = \overleftarrow{PQ} = \overrightarrow{QP}$. Like most things in maths, you can see what they are describing with a bit of common sense.

H: Multiples of vectors and inverse vectors

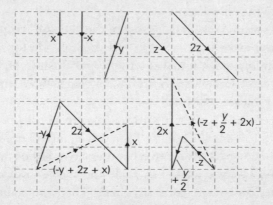

Here we're given the direction and length of three vectors **x**, **y**, and **z**. You can see that the inverse of **x** is − **x** which is the same length but has the arrow the other way round. Also 2**z** is the same direction as **z** but twice as long. Putting combinations of vectors together is simple, you just draw each bit at a time and go along following the arrows. It's rather fun in a quiet way.

Here comes the sort of basic vector question you might get. Have a go yourself and that way you'll find out any bits you don't understand:

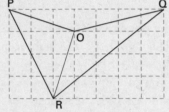

Write each of these combinations as one vector:
$$\vec{OR} + \vec{RQ} : \vec{RQ} - \vec{OQ} + \vec{PR} : \vec{PQ} + \overleftarrow{PR} - \vec{RQ}$$

Have you had a go? Really? Oh all right then, now read on and see how you got on . . .

The first one is simple enough. The two vectors take you from O to Q so the answer is $\vec{OQ}$.

For the second one, it helps to turn the "inverse" vector round so that you make $-\vec{OQ} = + \vec{QO}$. As you can add (or subtract) vectors in any order, it makes sense to put them in an order so that you can follow them round the diagram and see where they take you. You get $\vec{PR} + \vec{RQ} + \vec{QO} = \vec{PO}$.

Number three is a bit of a trick. To start with there are two inverse vectors and life is nicer if you can change them, so $\overleftarrow{PR} = \vec{RP}$ and $-\vec{RQ} = \vec{QR}$. When you put them in order you find the vectors take you round in a circle and you get back to where you started so haven't gone anywhere. Therefore adding these three vectors gives an answer of 0 or zero.

Here's one last little challenge for you:

> **Starting with $\vec{RP}$, describe how to draw this diagram without taking the pencil from the paper.**

Answer on page 315.

Vector questions often need a bit of geometric common sense.

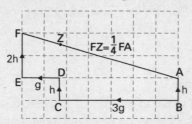

Describe the following vectors in terms of g and h:
$\vec{CF}$; $\vec{EA}$; $\vec{FA}$; $\vec{AZ}$; $\vec{EZ}$

Again, have a go at these yourself before you read on.

$\vec{CF}$ = 3**h** + **g**   All you do is follow your path from C to F and add up the vectors as you go along.

$\vec{EA}$ = – 4**g**   Again, just follow the path from E to A, but don't forget you need the inverse of some of the vectors, so put in those minus signs. Moving along ED, DC, CB and BA in turn gives – **g** – **h** – 3**g** + **h** so putting these together gives you – 4**g** .

$\vec{FA}$ = – 4**g** – 2**h** You could follow the path right round the diagram from F to A, but a short cut is to use

251

$\vec{FA} = \vec{FE} + \vec{EA}$. We've already worked out that $\vec{EA} = -4g$ and $\vec{FE}$ is simply $-2h$ so you can just put them together to get the answer.

$\vec{AZ} = 3g + \frac{3h}{2}$ $\vec{AF}$ is the inverse of $\vec{FA}$ which we've just worked out so $\vec{AF} = -(-4g - 2h) = 4g + 2h$. The diagram tells us that AZ is $\frac{3}{4}$ AF therefore $\vec{AZ} = \frac{3}{4} \vec{AF}$.

$\vec{EZ} = -g + \frac{3h}{2}$ Use $\vec{EZ} = \vec{EA} + \vec{AZ} = -4g + (3g + \frac{3h}{2}) = -g + \frac{3h}{2}$

H: Speed vectors

Vectors really get useful in sorting out problems involving forces or speeds. The measurements are going to involve angles and size, so a certain amount of trigonometry crops up. Here's a typical question:

A clockwork toy boat is pointed to sail directly across a stream. In still water the boat would travel at 10 cm/sec. The stream is flowing at 20 cm/sec. What is the actual speed and direction that the boat travels in? If the stream is 3 m wide, how long does the boat take to cross? How far down the stream does it land?

The first thing is to draw a little vector diagram:

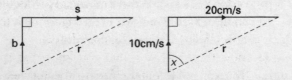

b shows the direction the boat would go if the stream were not flowing. **s** shows the direction of the stream which is at 90° to **b**. The different lengths of the lines indicate the different speeds. We know the magnitudes of **b** and **s**: |**b**| = 10 cm/s and |**s**| = 20 cm/s. (The two little lines either side indicate that we're just talking about the magnitudes.) The second triangle has these values put in and with a bit of trig we can calculate both the magnitude and direction of the resultant vector (**b** + **s**) which we'll call **r** for convenience.

Pythagoras tells us |**r**|^2 = 10^2 + 20^2 so |**r**| = 22·36 cm/sec.

The angle x shows how far off course the stream is pushing the boat and we can see than tan $x = \frac{20}{10} = 2$ so $x = 63·43°$. So the actual speed and direction that the boat travels in is 22·36 cm/sec at an angle of 63·43° to the intended direction.

To find how long the boat takes to cross, there are two ways of doing it:

Using the resultant vector r

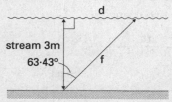

If the boat could go straight across the stream, it would only travel 3 m. However the boat is travelling at an angle of 63·43° so it has to go a lot further as shown in this diagram. If the real distance of travel is f, then cos 63·43° = $\frac{3}{f}$. Before reading on, work out f for yourself. You can also make your own little trig formula to work out d which is how far downstream the boat drifts.

Once you know the distance f, and you know the speed is 22·36 cm/sec, you can work out how long the journey takes. (Make sure you use the distance in cm.)

Using the components of the vector

Suprisingly, because the stream is flowing at right angles to the direction of crossing, it does not actually increase or reduce the time taken to cross! Therefore we can just use the vector which indicates the boat's speed directly over the stream and we know this is 10 cm/sec. As the stream is 3 m wide (which is 300 cm), the time taken will be $\frac{300}{10}$ = 30 seconds. This should agree with the answer you worked out!

Now we know that the boat travels for 30 seconds, we can work out how far down stream the current takes the boat. This time the speed of the boat itself doesn't matter, and in fact we could just leave the boat in the stream without the engine running for 30 seconds and see how far the current takes it. We know the current runs at 20 cm/s so the distance downstream it takes the boat is 20 × 30 cm = 600 cm or 6 m. Does this agree with your answer for d? By the way, you'll notice that we haven't bothered to work out f at all!

Look at these two triangles:

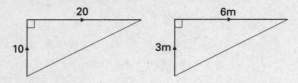

One shows the vectors involved and the other shows the real life measurements of the stream. Two completely different sorts of information, but the triangles are similar!

Don't put different sorts of vectors on the same diagram! So DON'T try to put the distance across the stream on the same diagram as the speeds as they cannot be directly linked up. It would make no sense, no more than if you tried to describe a smell by playing the piano.

> Fruity, with just a hint of old socks.

H: Vectors and bearings

Here's another way of presenting vector questions:

> **A helicopter needs to reach an island 100 km away on a bearing of 130° in 30 minutes. There is a wind blowing at 60 km/h on a bearing of 200°. What speed and what course should the pilot set?**

This sort of problem needs a bit of clear thinking.

The question is about speeds, so let's see what speed this journey needs. If there was no wind, the helicopter would need to travel a distance of 100 km in 30 minutes (which is 0·5 hours) so the speed would be $\frac{100}{0·5}$ = 200 km/h. We'll call the vector for the journey **j** and we know this is 200 km/h on a bearing of 130°.

Let's call the speed and bearing that the pilot sets vector **a** and call the wind vector **w**. We know that **a** + **w** must equal **j**.

It's time to draw a diagram of the vectors. There are three vectors involved, and as we know **j** and **w** we can draw in **a** to complete the triangle.

> **TOP TIP**
> Don't be scared to make diagrams BIG! That way you can fit lots of the details in.

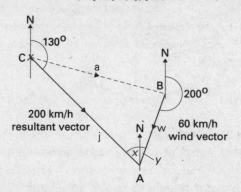

First we drew the resultant vector **j**, and then we drew the wind vector **w** to meet it. Finally we drew **a**, the vector we're looking for. The arrows are marked so that **a** + **w** = **j**. All we have to work out now is the length and direction of **a**. Your turn!

Hint: Use the bearings to work out angle BÂC first. As the diagram shows, this is easier if you draw in the "north" arrow and work out the bits on each side. You then need to use both the sine and cosine rules for the answer. (Answers on page 315.)

Data drives me dotty!

Have you ever been stopped in the street by somebody holding a clipboard who asks you about washing powder or pollution or holidays? These days surveys and market research seem to rule the planet and there's even a branch of maths devoted to this stuff, so here's what it's all about.

F: Questionnaires

The secret of creating a good questionnaire is to supply the right set of answers, each with a tick box. The answers provided should cover all options and there are several dos and don'ts you need to be aware of:

- **The questions must be absolutely clear.** If you ask, "At breakfast do you like tea or coffee?" it could mean "Which do you prefer at breakfast, tea or coffee?" Answer options: [Tea] [Coffee] [Neither]. Or it could mean "Do you like a drink at breakfast such as tea or coffee?" Answer options: [Yes] [No].

- **The questions must not be subjective (i.e. they should not**

be asking an opinion). If you asked, "Do you own a lot of clothes?", some people would regard a drawerful as a lot, others would think that a whole wardrobeful was bordering on nudity. This question would need to be more specific, e.g. "How many pairs of pants have you got?" Answer options: [0] [1–2] [3–4] [5–6] [7–8] [9–10] [more than 10].

- **The questions should only have a few possible answers.** If the question was, "What's the most boring thing on telly?", you'd need to supply hundreds of tick boxes! You'd be better asking, "Which of these is the most boring?" Answer options: [chat shows] [the news] [soaps] [sport] [cookery/gardening/DIY] [comedy] [anything with Michael Barrymore in it].

- **The questions should not be biased.** Suppose the owner of the Venice Hilton wanted to know how popular his hotel was and you asked, "Where would you most like to spend a romantic weekend?" There's not much point giving these answer options: [An airport departure lounge] [The Venice Hilton] [Manchester Gas Works] [The dentist's].

F: Surveys

Once you've got your questionnaire ready, you have to check that any data you collect is a true indication of what's going on. A survey might come back saying that 92% of all drivers wear wellington boots. Of course that's ridiculous, but that's the result you *could* get if the survey was taken on a remote country lane in February. How about 85% of the population are men who wear make-up and huge trousers? Again, it's no good if you just happen to be doing your survey in a hotel holding a clown convention.

Surveys also cover testing things and often you need to think about how many you need to test. Here are some examples to think about. You should not only be able to give an answer, but also to justify it!

1. You find a box with 100 food cans in it, but all the labels have come off. They could be beans, or they could be cat food, or some of each. How many do you need to open before you can be reasonably sure that all, some or none of them are beans?

2. You are testing the waterproof seals around submarine windows. How many should you check to be sure that the submarine is safe?

3. If you have a full box of matches that may have got damp, how many should you test to see if they still work?

Answers on page 315.

From surveys to graphs

We're going to do a mock survey then use the data to show some of the ways that you can process it. The Sloppychops Card Company has commissioned you to do a survey about valentines. They want to know how many valentines the average person sends and receives and if there's a link between the two. So, armed with your pink clipboard and cheesiest smile, you hit the streets. . .

F: Collecting data

Your first question could have been, "In your whole life, have you received lots of valentines?" – but can you see the problem with it? It's too subjective. Some people might think getting 3 is a lot, others might think just getting 120 is a social disaster. Also their yes/no answer doesn't tell you much.

Instead you ask "How many valentines have you ever sent? How many have you ever received?"

You could set out tick boxes with answers: [0–1] [2–3] [4–5] [6–7] and so on, but just for now let's assume you write down the numbers given.

You survey 50 people, and the results are listed like this:

person	sent	received	person	sent	received	person	sent	received
1	5	4	18	10	9	35	6	6
2	11	2	19	15	17	36	12	10
3	1	0	20	13	14	37	8	9
4	18	14	21	1	4	38	8	6
5	7	3	22	6	4	39	5	6
6	8	8	23	12	8	40	6	5
7	1	3	24	2	19	41	11	10
8	6	12	25	4	6	42	5	4
9	6	9	26	3	6	43	5	4
10	7	6	27	4	5	44	0	5
11	7	4	28	5	16	45	3	8
12	3	5	29	10	10	46	8	5
13	5	5	30	5	1	47	8	7
14	6	7	31	3	7	48	10	11
15	3	1	32	12	13	49	13	12
16	9	11	33	9	7	50	10	7
17	8	8	34	3	3			

There's the data, but now what do you do with it? (Apart from tell person 24 that they are probably lying.)

F: Scatter graphs

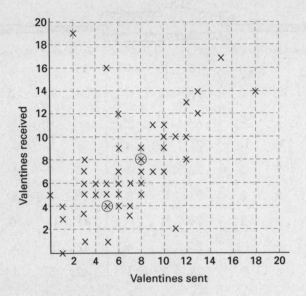

This graph has "Valentines sent" along the bottom and "Valentines received" up the side. There's a point for each person, so person number 1 has a point at position (5,4), person 2 at (11,2) and so on. A couple of points are used more than once, so these are ringed for emphasis.

A scatter graph like this is used to show "correlation" between the two results. This means "how much one value affects the other". Here you'll notice that most of the points on the graph form a diagonal band going from bottom left to top right. This indicates that if a person sends more valentines, they are likely to receive more back. If more of one thing leads to more of another, this is a **positive correlation**. As the band on this graph is fairly wide, this is only a **moderate positive correlation.**

Here are two more examples of scatter graphs:

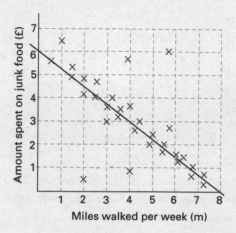

This scatter graph plots the miles each person walks in a week against how much they spend on junk food. Clearly the *more* people walk, the *less* money they spend and the band of results is quite narrow. Most of the points lie in quite a narrow band so this is a **strong negative correlation**. It's even possible to draw a line through the centre of the band of points. This is called the **line of best fit** and you can use it to make an equation linking miles walked (m) against pounds spent (p). (Check back at the graphs section to remind yourself how to do this.) The line goes from point $(8,0)$ to $(0,6)$ so the gradient is $-\frac{6}{8} = -\frac{3}{4}$. The y intercept in this case is the p intercept and it is $p = 6$. This gives an equation for the line of $y = -\frac{3m}{4} + 6$. If you met a member of the group and were told that they walked about 2 miles per week, you could use this equation to predict that they spent around £$(-2 \times \frac{3}{4} + 6)$ = £4.50 on junk food.

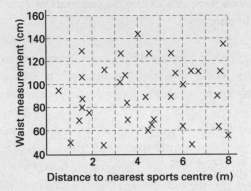

Distance to nearest sports centre (m)

This scatter graph shows the distance a person lives from the nearest sports centre against their waist measurement. The points show no clear correlation at all.

F: Pie charts

If you've got a computer, when you check the disk space it is often displayed on screen as a "pie chart".

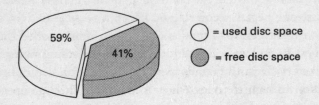

It's a convenient way of seeing how the whole of something is divided up. In this case you imagine the whole of your computer hard disk as a "pie", and it's cut into two sections, the bit you've used and the bit left free. The bits are usually shown in different colours for clarity, with the percentage of each piece written in.

Sloppychops want you to make a pie chart of your valentine survey results showing:

- how many people have received more valentines than they sent
- how many people have sent and received an equal number
- how many losers have sent more valentines than they got back

Notice that each person in our survey fits into one of these categories and no one fits into more than one. This is very important. You can only draw a pie chart if this is true.

You need to go through each person's results in your data and see which category they fall into. The usual way to keep track of the number in each category is to do a "tally".

	TOTAL	FRACTION	%
Received More : ~~IIII~~ ~~IIII~~ ~~IIII~~ ~~IIII~~ I	21	$\frac{21}{50}$	42%
Equal : ~~IIII~~ I	6	$\frac{6}{50}$	12%
Sent More : ~~IIII~~ ~~IIII~~ ~~IIII~~ ~~IIII~~ III	23	$\frac{23}{50}$	46%

You make three rows, one for each category ("Received more", "Equal", "Sent more") then go through the results one by one putting a "I" in the correct row for each person. Every fifth "I" strikes through the previous four to show a little group of five which makes the counting up easier. At the end you add up the people in each row, and here we get 21:6:23. Since we know the total number of people surveyed was 50, this means we can make three fractions representing each group. These are $\frac{21}{50}$, $\frac{6}{50}$ and $\frac{23}{50}$. If we multiply these fractions by 100 we get percentages: 42%, 12% and 46%.

Computers often show pie charts as pretty 3-dimensional graphics, but for us mere humans it's easier and more accurate just to show a circle that's divided up. Our data is divided into three categories so our pie chart will have three sectors. As there are 360° in a full circle, the centre angles of the three sectors will be:

More received: $360 \times \frac{21}{50}$ $= 151\cdot2°$
Equal: $360 \times \frac{6}{50}$ $= 43\cdot2°$
More sent: $360 \times \frac{23}{50}$ $= 165\cdot6°$

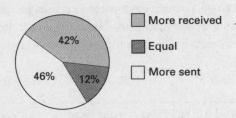

You don't need to draw the angles exactly in your exam, but it's still worth getting a protractor out rather than guessing.

F: Groups
(From now on these examples will just use the data about valentines sent, but you might like to practise making your own graphs and tables using the data about valentines received by each person.)

To make information easier to manage, you can "group" it. Suppose our questionnaire had used tick boxes instead of writing down numbers, the results for the first few people surveyed might have looked like this:

Person	Valentines sent				
	0–3	4–7	8–11	12–15	16–19
1	[ ]	[✓]	[ ]	[ ]	[ ]
2	[ ]	[ ]	[✓]	[ ]	[ ]
3	[✓]	[ ]	[ ]	[ ]	[ ]
4	[ ]	[ ]	[ ]	[ ]	[✓]
5	[ ]	[✓]	[ ]	[ ]	[ ]

You would then go through all 50 people and count up how many are in each group. In other words: how many people sent between 0 and 3 valentines, how many sent between 4 and 7 valentines . . . and so on. The data we've got produces these grouped results:

Valentines sent:	0–3	4–7	8–11	12–15	16–19
Number in group:	11	18	14	6	1

F: Pictograms

This is just a pretty way of presenting data for people who are scared of graphs. Using the grouped results we've got gives this pictogram:

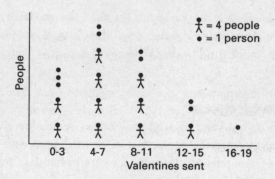

It's unlikely that you'll need to draw a pictogram in an exam, but you may be asked to take some data off one. In this case they could ask "How many valentines do most people send?" and the answer is "between 4 and 7".

F: Bar charts

A bar chart "or equal interval histogram" would use data in the same way as a line graph or pictogram, but you get a solid bar indicating the size of each group.

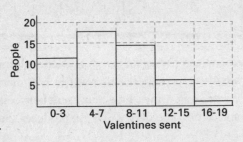

F: The mode

Pictograms and bar charts both make one thing clear: which is the most popular group. Sloppychops Cards could look at either of these graphs and see that most people send between 4 and 7 valentines.

The result that is most popular is called **the mode**. If you're doing the intermediate or higher level there's more on modes in the "Means, modes and medians" section later on.

Cumulative frequency

I: So far we've just been counting valentines, which has given us sets of discrete measurements, but now we'll play with some continuous measurements. If you've forgotten what they are, look back to page 65.

24 bag of chips were bought from different shops and each portion was weighed to see how they vary: (weights in grams): 677 665 712 637 572 699 624 637 649 670 648 721 525 685 632 675 715 686 731 700 652 595 762 584

The first thing to do is to split these weights into groups. You might be told a suitable group size to use, but otherwise you'll be expected to choose a suitable **interval** – in other words the range of values for each group. The way to approach this is to find the smallest and largest results, which in this case are 525 g and 762 g. If we round these off to lower and higher limits, we can say that the weights all fall between 500 g and 800 g. Let's split this range into six groups (or "classes") with intervals of 50 g. We can now put this data on a table, and it can help to use a tally to count up how many weights fall in each class.

Weight	Tally	Frequency	Cumulative Frequency
500–550	I	1	1
551–600	III	3	4
601–650	₦₦ I	6	10
651–700	₦₦ IIII	9	19
701–750	IIII	4	23
751–800	I	1	24

You'll see the number of weights that fall into each class is called the **frequency**. There is also a column called **cumulative frequency (c.f.)**. The c.f. for each class is the frequency of that class *plus* all the frequencies for the smaller classes. If you look at the 651–700 g class, the frequency of 9 shows that 9 bags of chips weighed between 651 and 700 g, and the c.f. of 19 means that 19 bags of chips weighed anything up to 700 g. Of course the c.f. of the last class (in this case the 750–800 g) is the same as the total number of bags of chips weighed.

To draw a cumulative frequency graph of these results, you have to plot cumulative frequency against weight.

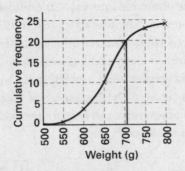

Be sure that:

- The c.f. always goes on the vertical axis.
- The points are joined with a smooth curve rather than a set of straight lines.
- For each class you plot the point *using the upper limit value of the range*, so for the 550–600 g class which has a c.f. of 4, the point used on the graph is (600,4) not (550,4) or (575,4). (Examiners ALWAYS check you've got this right! A common mistake is to plot the point for each class between the upper and lower limits. This is an evil, bad, naughty and despicable thing to do.)

I: The median and upper and lower quartiles

Suppose you're asked how many bags of chips weigh up to 710 g: you can make an estimate using the graph. Just draw a line up from the 710 g and see where it hits the curve (see the dotted lines on the graph) and it tells you the c.f. for 710 g is 20. This means there are about 20 bags of chips weighing anything up to 710 g.

The median

Something of great interest to people is the middle or "median" value. Let's see a simple example first:

If you've got 7 people standing in a line in order of height, the person with the median height would be the one in the middle. This person would be the fourth along from the end, and it wouldn't matter which end of the line you counted from. It's usually pretty obvious which sample is in the middle but it looks good if you use this formula:

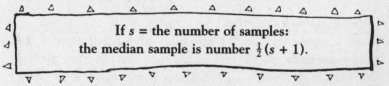

> **If s = the number of samples:**
> **the median sample is number $\frac{1}{2}(s + 1)$.**

As we had 7 people in the line, $s = 7$. So the median person is $\frac{1}{2}(7 + 1) = 4$. Note: If your survey used more than 50 samples then it's close enough to say the median sample number $= \frac{s}{2}$.

Now let's see how to get a median value for bags of chips off our c.f. diagram.

- First you need to get a median value for the c.f. (This is occasionally called the "2nd quartile" as you'll see in a minute.) As we had 24 samples, use the formula with $s = 24$, so the median c.f. value comes to $12\frac{1}{2}$.
- You draw a line across from the median c.f. value and see where it hits the curve.

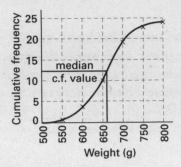

Here the median value is at 665 g. This means that if you went out to buy a packet of chips, it's most likely to weigh about 665 g.

> **TOP TIP**
> To check your median c.f. value, it should be about halfway up the c.f. axis.

Upper and lower quartiles

A quick glance back at the raw data tells us that most of the weights are in the middle region, and there are just a few that are much bigger or smaller. The c.f. graph gives a tidy way of saying what this middle region is.

In the same way that we needed to work out the median c.f. value – or 2nd quartile – we can work out the 1st quartile (lower) and 3rd quartile (upper) values. The word *quartile* gives the clue as to what's coming because it involves *quarters*.

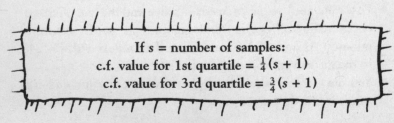

> If s = number of samples:
> c.f. value for 1st quartile = $\frac{1}{4}(s + 1)$
> c.f. value for 3rd quartile = $\frac{3}{4}(s + 1)$

(Again, if $s > 50$ then you can ignore the "+ 1"s.)

As $s = 24$, we have the 1st quartile with c.f. $= 6\frac{1}{4}$ and the 3rd with c.f. $= 18\frac{3}{4}$.

We plot these values on the graph and see that they hit the curve. . .

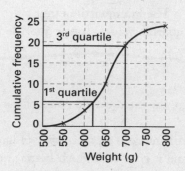

. . . at 620 g and 695 g. This tells us two things:

- half the packets of chips weighed betweeen 620 g and 695 g
- the section between these values is the **interquartile range** which we can work out as 695 g – 620 g = 75 g

I: Ranges of data

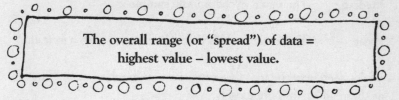

The overall range (or "spread") of data = highest value – lowest value.

With our chip survey, the overall range is 762 g – 525 g = 237 g.

If you want an idea of how the weights of bags of chips generally vary, the overall range can be misleading. Suppose we had come across one miserable bag of chips that had just weighed 3 g, the overall range would have been 759 g. This wouldn't give a very good indication as to how the weights generally vary.

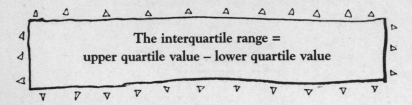

**The interquartile range =
upper quartile value – lower quartile value**

As we've just seen, the interquartile range of the chips is 695 g – 620 g = 75 g.

The interquartile range is a precise way of ignoring the more extreme values and it gives us a much better indication of how closely all the different measurements fall.

Means, modes and medians

The word "average" is rather vague and confusing. In maths it can can be one of three things:

Mode   The most popular value.

Median   The value of the middle sample.

Mean   The exact middle value worked out with a formula.

We've seen how the first two can arrive on graphs, but we'll look at them all again more closely.

I: Using discrete data

Here are the goals scored by 20 footballers last season:

PLAYER:	GOALS:	PLAYER:	GOALS:
a	0	k	2
b	0	l	4
c	0	m	4
d	0	n	6
e	0	o	9
f	0	p	10
g	0	q	13
h	0	r	18
i	1	s	21
j	1	t	45

Mode

This is the group with the biggest frequency. The biggest is the group of 8 players that scored 0 goals so the mode is 0 goals.

If two or more groups had the same biggest frequency (i.e. suppose 8 of the other players scored 4 goals each) then there is no mode value.

Median

This is the value of the middle sample. This is easier with odd numbers of samples, because if there had been just 19 players involved, then the result of the 10th player would have been the median. As we have an even number we look at the two in the middle which are j who scored 1 goal and k who scored 2 goals. The median is halfway between these two values, so the median number of goals is $1\frac{1}{2}$.

Mean

For this value we add up all the goals and divide by the number of players. We get $\frac{134}{20}$ = 6·7 goals.

> **Look back at the chips data. What are the mode, median and mean values?**

Answers on page 315.

I: Using grouped data

> **A used car salesman has made records of the mileages in his cars and then grouped them accordingly:**

Description	Mileage (in 1,000s)	No. in group ("frequency")
Brand new	0–9,999	2
Hardly driven	10,000–19,999	3
Nice runner	20,000–29,999	8
One owner	30,000–39,999	14
Super buy	40,000–49,999	11
Vintage classic	50,000-59,999	6

> **Find the mode, median and mean values, as well as the overall range and interquartile range.**

The mode is easy: the "30,000–39,999" group has the highest frequency, so that's it.

Finding the exact median is really dodgy with grouped data. The only thing you can really say is that the median will be in the "30,000–39,999" group. Don't worry, if they want you to plot a special graph you'll be told exactly what to do.

The mean is also tricky. Because we don't know exactly how many miles each car has done, we have to get a best estimate for each car. We then add all the individual estimates up and divide by the total number of cars. Here's the sequence of sums to do:

- Take each group in turn and work out the mid-value. This gives an idea of how many miles each car in the group might have done. For the 0–9,999 group the mid-value is $\frac{1}{2}(0 + 9,999) = 5,000$. For the 10,000–19,999 group the mid-value is $\frac{1}{2}(10,000 + 19,999) = 15,000$ and so on.

- Multiply the mid-value of each group by its frequency. This gives us an estimate of the total number of miles travelled by all the cars in the group. For the 0–9,999 group the total is $2 \times 5,000 = 10,000$. For the 10,000–19,999 group the total is $3 \times 15,000 = 45,000$.

- On you go. Work out the total mileage for each group, then add them all up. Also add up the total number of cars. It helps to set the results out in a table like this:

Mileage	Mid-value	Number in group	Mid-value × number
0–9,999	5,000	2	10,000

- Finally you divide the total miles by the total number of cars. What do you get? (Answer on page 315.)

The highest possible mileage is 59,999 and the lowest is 0, so the overall range here is 59,999.

If you add a line to the original data table to show cumulative frequency and then plot a c.f./mileage graph, you could also get the interquartile range. As a bonus you'll get a value for the median too. Have a go yourself before looking at the answers on page 316.

Don't panic if your answers are not exactly the same as the ones in the back of the book. In graph questions, examiners accept answers which are close to the right one as it is difficult to be completely accurate.

Histograms

H: At first glance histograms look like bar charts, but some of the bars are wider than others. In fact there are several other differences which allow histograms to display a much wider range of data.

Here are the recorded speeds of vehicles on a motorway:

Speed range (mph)	Frequency	Speed range (mph)	Frequency
0–9·99	2	50–59·99	156
10–19·99	12	60–69·99	203
20–29·99	38	70–79·99	196
30–39·99	72	80–89·99	85
40–49·99	108	90–99·99	3

You might like to try plotting these results on a normal bar chart. You'll find that the 2 cars doing less than 10 mph and the 3 cars doing over 90 mph hardly register compared to the bigger groups.

Anyone looking at your chart might think that no traffic goes under 10 mph or over 90 mph. This isn't true, and as traffic going so slowly or so fast can be extremely hazardous it would be wrong to let these groups be overlooked.

What do you mean, "hazardous"?

The way to show that there are some vehicles in these very small groups is to amalgamate neighbouring groups together. Suppose the smallest number of vehicles you want to show in a group is 40, you would reset your table like this (all will be explained soon):

Speed	Frequency	Interval	Frequency density
0–29·99	52	30	1·73
30–39·99	72	10	7·2
40–49·99	108	10	10·8
50–59·99	156	10	15·6
60–69·99	203	10	20·3
70–79·99	196	10	19·6
80–99·99	88	20	4·4

- To start with we've put the slowest three groups together to make one group with speeds in the range of 0–29·99 mph. The number of vehicles in this group is 2 + 12 + 38 = 52. We've done the same for the two fastest groups.

- There's now a new column showing the interval of each group. All the groups in the original data had intervals of 10 mph but the new groups we've just formed have bigger intervals.

- There's also a column showing **frequency density**. This is worked out for each result as follows:

$$\text{Frequency density} = \frac{\text{frequency of group}}{\text{group interval}}$$

So for the 80–99·99 group the frequency density = 88 ÷ 20 = 4·4.

This is the data you need to plot a histogram, so let's see what it looks like...

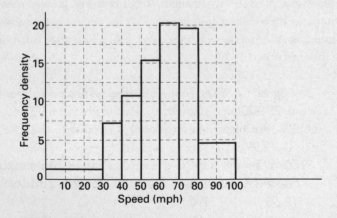

TOP TIPS
Make histograms as neat as possible.

Always put the frequency density up the side.

Always draw the axes to an even scale. If a group has an interval three times bigger than another, then the column should be three times wider. In this case it would have been utterly criminal to miss out the values "10" and "20" to make the first column the same width as the rest!

H: What do histograms tell you?

The secret of understanding histograms is to check the *area* of each column because the area indicates the frequency of the group. It follows that the column with the biggest area indicates the mode group.

With a normal bar chart, the columns are the same width, so obviously the tallest is the mode. However with histograms you need to allow for the width as well. Here the last column is twice as wide as the column representing the 30–40 mph group. If the 30–40 mph was to have a higher frequency than the 80–100 mph group it would need to be at least twice as high, but you can tell by looking that it isn't. Therefore more vehicles were travelling between 80–100 mph than were travelling between 30–40 mph.

Look at this histogram and decide for yourself:

Which is the mode group? What is the maximum speed that about half the vehicles travel under?

Answers on page 316.

The examiners might even show you a histogram and ask for the total frequency – in other words, how many samples were used? What you have to do is work out the area of each column to get the frequency of each column, then add them all together to get the total. Looking at this histogram, the area of the last column is 20 along (remember NOT to use the values 80 or 100, what you want is the interval between them) × 4·4 high which gives a frequency of 20 × 4·4 = 88.

It's a bit of a dull job adding all these areas up but it's simple enough, so you should see this as a way to get a few easy marks.

Standard deviation (The ugliest formula)

H: This bit of maths includes the ugliest looking formula you come across in GCSE so let's look at it and get it over with. The Greek letter "σ" (sigma) is almost exclusively used to mean **standard deviation** (s.d.), so here it comes:

$$\sigma = \sqrt{\frac{\Sigma f(x - \bar{x})^2}{n}}$$

Sure it's nasty, but all this formula is doing is presenting a set of instructions in a mathematical way. We'll see these instructions written out fully in a moment, but first the big question: why does anybody bother with all this?

Exactly.

H: What is deviation?

Suppose you got 25 rugby players and found their mean weight was 110 kg. You would probably find most of them fall within ± 20 kg of this value, so most of their weights "deviate" from the mean by less than 20%. However, if you got 25 people ranging from babies to adults and found their average weight was 60 kg you might find that to include most of them you have to use ± 30 kg of this value. Here the spread deviates 50% each way so it's much greater.

If you are running a clothes shop, it's useful to know what sizes of clothes to order in. For the rugby players you only need a fairly limited range of sizes because the small deviation tells you that they are all of fairly similar build.

Of course, if you're kitting out whole families you need a massive range of sizes because the deviation is much larger.

H: What the formula is telling you to do

Whenever you see "Σ" in a formula, this means you have to work out lots of little bits then add them up, so it's always best to work out formulae like this using a table. We'll see an example in a minute, but first we'll see what the exact instructions are:

- First you calculate the mean of all the results. With the rugby players you would add up all their weights and divide by the number of players. This mean is represented in the formula by "$\bar{x}$".

- Next you take each individual result in turn and subtract the mean to get the deviation and then square the answer. This is represented in the formula by "$(x - \bar{x})^2$". If any results occur more than once you can just multiply the squared deviation by the frequency which is why the "f" comes into the formula. (So if three rugby players weigh exactly the same, work out the deviation for one, square it, then multiply it by 3.)

- Add up all the squared deviations (that's the "Σ" bit).

- Divide the total of the squares by the number of samples.

- Finally take the square root to get the "standard deviation".

Let's see how an example works:

> **A survey of 15 people leaving a car boot sale shows how many items each person bought:**
> **4, 6, 2, 4, 1, 7, 13, 6, 5, 5, 6, 3, 7, 6, 5**
>
> **Calculate the mean. Also find the standard variation to 2 decimal places. What do they tell you?**

284

First work out the mean by adding them all up and dividing the total by 15. You get $\bar{x} = 5\cdot3$.

Once you've got the mean, you can start filling out a table. Here we've labelled the columns with words and then bits of the formula, but in an exam you only need to put the bits of formula in:

Items bought	Deviation	Dev²	Frequency	Freq × dev²
x	$x - \bar{x}$	$(x - \bar{x})^2$	f	$f(x - \bar{x})^2$
1	$-4\cdot3$	18·49	1	18·49
2	$-3\cdot3$	10·89	1	10·89
3	$-2\cdot3$	5·29	1	5·29
4	$-1\cdot3$	1·69	2	3·38
5	$-0\cdot3$	0·09	3	0·27
6	0·7	0·49	4	1·96
7	1·7	2·89	2	5·78
13	7·7	59·29	1	59·29
		Totals	15	105·35

For example, four people bought 6 items each, so in the "items bought" column $x = 6$ and then along this line $f = 4$. The deviation is $6 - 5\cdot3 = 0\cdot7$. When you square this you get $0\cdot49$. Then you multiply this by the frequency which is 4 to get $1\cdot96$.

The totals are the bits we need next:

- 15 is how many people were surveyed = n.
- 105·35 is the total of all the deviations squared = $\Sigma f(x - \bar{x})^2$.
- Putting these into the formula gives $\sigma = \sqrt{\frac{105\cdot35}{15}}$ which comes to 2·65.

This tells you that the mean number of items people bought was 5·3 items. It also tells us that generally people bought within the range of 2·65 items more or less. To make more sense of this, you might say the average number of items bought was between 5 and 6, and generally people bought between about 3 and 8 items.

H: Using a calculator for standard deviation

Unless a question particularly tells you to use the formula to work out the standard deviation, you can use the special buttons on your calculator instead. Be careful. To start with you'll probably have to put your calculator into S.D. or STAT mode and then different calculators need you to enter the information in different ways. Make sure you know how to use the one you are going to take into the exam and practise with it beforehand.

> **TOP TIP**
> To help you enter the data correctly, make a table of "x" and "f" values before you start.

TOP TIP

If you make a mistake entering data and you're not sure how to clear the last entry, turn the calculator off and start again. If you're clever you might have worked out how to change data entries, but, with statistics, the "C" and "AC" and even "SAC" buttons don't always do what you might expect. The only sure way to make sure everything is right is to turn the thing off so its memory completely empties.

Check your calculator is using the correct formula.

Some calculators give two values of standard deviation. One uses the formula:

$$\sqrt{\frac{\Sigma f(x - \bar{x})^2}{n}}$$

and the other uses the formula:

$$\sqrt{\frac{\Sigma f(x - \bar{x})^2}{n - 1}}$$

The second formula gets used for massive population surveys and does not come into GCSE. If your calculator gives both options, they may be labelled σ_n and $\sigma_{(n-1)}$, or they may be labelled σ and s. You might even need to use the 2nd function or shift key to get σ_n rather than $\sigma_{(n-1)}$. The two answers you get are very similar to each other: *if in doubt use the LOWER one.*

It's worth doing this little experiment to make sure your calculator is doing what you want: get the s.d. of these four values: 5, 5, 15, 15. (You might enter: 5 × 2 DATA 15 × 2 DATA). The mean should be 10 and the s.d. should be 5. If your calculator gives the s.d. as 5·77 then it has worked out $\sigma_{(n-1)}$ which is what you *don't* want. If you get any other answer, then make sure you're pushing the right buttons!

A bit of practice
First, try your calculator out on the car boot sale data we've just seen. Hopefully your answers will agree with this book!

Now try the bags of chips on page 269! What do you get for the mean and standard deviations? (Answers on page 316.)

Probability

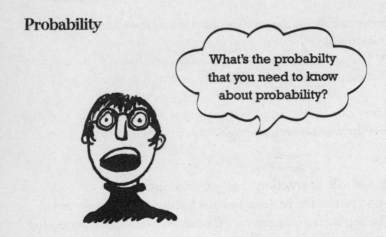

What's the probabilty that you need to know about probability?

F: It's about 100% because even if you don't get a direct question on it, it's often used in fractions or data, so make sure you know the basics.

> **TOP TIP**
> The words "probability" and "chance" mean the same in a maths question. Use the same word in your answer as the examiner used in the question.

If you throw a normal dice. . .

- There are six possible *outcomes* because there are 6 different ways it can land.
- It will *definitely* land on a number between 1 and 6. This is *certain*, it's *a sure thing* and mathematically speaking it has *100% probability* or *a chance of 1*.
- It will *definitely* not land on 7. That's *impossible*, it has *0% probability* or a *zero chance*.
- It has a *fair chance* of landing on one of the odd numbers. This is a *50% probability*, or an *even chance* or a *chance of* $\frac{1}{2}$.
- It is *unlikely* to land on 6. The *odds are against it*, it's *unfair* to expect a 6 to come up. There is a *chance of 16·67% or* $\frac{1}{6}$.

So much for the basic descriptions, but now we'll see how maths deals with it all.

F: Chance in fractions and percentages
Any chance can be described as a fraction using this formula:

$$\frac{\textit{number of useful outcomes}}{\textit{total number of possible outcomes}}$$

If you have a shuffled pack of 52 cards and want to pull a jack, what's the chance? There are 4 jacks, so the number of useful outcomes is 4. The number of possible outcomes is 52, so it's $\frac{4}{52}$.

TOP TIP

Don't reduce chance fractions until the very end of a question. It's clearer to see what's going on if you put $\frac{4}{52}$, especially if the problem involves some more calculations. However, once you've got to the end of the question, you could then show the examiners you know about fractions by reducing $\frac{4}{52}$ to $\frac{1}{13}$.

Often chances are given as percentages, so you just multiply the fraction by 100. Here the chance of getting a jack is $\frac{4}{52} \times 100$ = 7·69%.

Try these yourself:

What is the chance of throwing an even number on a normal 6-sided dice?

A bag of sweets has 10 different colours including green and yellow – if you pick one, what's the chance that it isn't green or yellow?

Work out the percentages for both.

Answers on page 316.

F: Chances adding to 1

Whether you're tossing a coin or a dice or just wondering if it will rain:

> **The chances of all the possible outcomes must add up to 1.**

Another way of saying this is that if an outcome has a probability of p then the probability of it NOT happening is $(1 - p)$.

If you throw a normal dice, it has an equal chance of landing on any of the six sides. Therefore the chance of tossing, say, a 4 is $\frac{1}{6}$. The chances of NOT getting a 4 are therefore $(1 - \frac{1}{6}) = \frac{5}{6}$. Surprise surprise: when you add these two you get $\frac{1}{6} + \frac{5}{6} = 1$.

If the weather report says there is a 30% chance of thunder storms, this means there must be a 70% chance of no thunder storms because 30% + 70% =100% which is the same as 1.

When the outcomes of an event are split into "yes" and "no" , these are known as **complementary** outcomes. For instance, if you go out on a blind date and there's a 3% chance your date *is* drop-dead gorgeous, the complementary outcome is the 97% chance that your date *is not* drop-dead gorgeous. When it comes to throwing a 4 on a dice, either you *do* get a 4 or the complementary outcome is that you *don't* get a 4. Of course the total chances of complementary outcomes always add up to 1.

F: The two different sorts of events
Mutually exclusive events

Imagine you have ten cards numbered 1–10 which are turned face down and shuffled. You remove one card but *don't* replace it. You then remove another. Can they both be 10? No, it's impossible, so it has a probability of 0.

You could pull out the 10 the first time *or* the second time, but not both. These outcomes are called **mutually exclusive** because if one happens, then the other cannot happen.

Your goldfish is looking a bit wheezy and won't last the week. What day will it finally go belly up? If it conks out on Tuesday, it can't conk out on Monday, Wednesday, Thursday or Friday because they are all mutually exclusive. Remember: goldfish – death – mutually exclusive.

I feel fine. Honestly.

Independent events

You have the same ten cards face down and shuffled. You remove one card, look at it, *then replace it*. The cards are shuffled and again you remove a card. Could you pick the 10 both times?

Yes, you can – there is a small chance you will pick the 10 on both occasions. Providing you always replace the card you picked, there is still the same chance of getting another 10 on your next attempt.

Tossing a coin or a dice also create independent events as on each throw they both give equal chances regardless of how they have fallen before.

F: Several mutually exclusive events

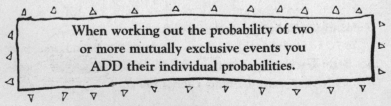

When working out the probability of two or more mutually exclusive events you ADD their individual probabilities.

You pick one card from a shuffled pack of 52 cards. What is the chance of it being the king of hearts OR the 3 of diamonds?

As the card cannot be the king of hearts AND the 3 of diamonds, these events are mutually exclusive, so add their chances.

The chance of the king of hearts is $\frac{1}{52}$. The chance of the 3 of diamonds is also $\frac{1}{52}$. The chance of getting one or the other is $\frac{1}{52} + \frac{1}{52} = \frac{2}{52} = \frac{1}{26}$.

Fred has 5 white shirts, 3 yellow shirts, 1 purple shirt, 4 blue shirts and 2 orange shirts. He doesn't care what he looks like. What's the chance he's wearing white or yellow? What's the chance that he isn't wearing purple or orange?

Your go. (Answers on page 316.)

F: Several independent events

> When working out the probability of two or more independent events happening at once you MULTIPLY their individual probabilities.

Cathy's Cafe has this menu:

Starters: soup, melon, prawns
Main: fish, curry, burger, lasagne

If you saw a man staggering out of the cafe, what's the chance he's had the melon and the curry (assuming all the dishes are equally popular)?

Choosing from the menu involves two events: the starter and the main course. As the choice of main course isn't affected by the starter, these are independent events. The chance of him having the melon is $\frac{1}{3}$. The chance of him having the curry is $\frac{1}{4}$. So the chance of him having both is $\frac{1}{3} \times \frac{1}{4} = \frac{1}{12}$.

Just to show you that this method works, we'll draw a table called a sample space or probability space:

		Main			
		fish	curry	burger	lasagne
	soup	sf	sc	sb	sl
Starter	melon	mf	mc	mb	ml
	prawns	pf	pc	pb	pl

This shows that there are 12 possible outcomes and only one of them is melon and curry. So the probability of that combination is $\frac{1}{12}$, just as we found from multiplying. In straightforward questions like this, it's easiest to multiply. But if it's difficult to work out how many acceptable outcomes there are, it can be easier to draw the table. We'll come back to this later.

First of all, let's think about dice.

If you throw one die, there are six possible outcomes, so the probability of throwing a 3 is $\frac{1}{6}$ and the probability of throwing a 4 is $\frac{1}{6}$ too.

If you throw two dice, they are independent of each other so the probability of throwing a 3 with the first dice and a 4 with the second is $\frac{1}{6} \times \frac{1}{6} = \frac{1}{36}$.

But be careful if you are asked to work out the probability of throwing a 3 and a 4 with two dice: this time the order doesn't matter so 3 on the first and 4 on the second is acceptable, and so is 4 on the first and 3 on the second. There are two ways to tackle this and both of them are equally correct.

Firstly, as these two outcomes are mutually exclusive, you can add their probabilities. So the probability of throwing a 3 and a 4 in any order is $\frac{1}{36} + \frac{1}{36} = \frac{2}{36} = \frac{1}{18}$.

Secondly, you could say there are 2 acceptable outcomes out of 36 possible outcomes, so the probability is $\frac{2}{36} = \frac{1}{18}$. Now try this one yourself:

> **You throw two dice at once. Work out the probability of throwing a double.**

Answers on page 317.

F: Tree diagrams

These are another way of illustrating how different outcomes can arise.

> **A bloke in a dodgy suit shows you two aces and a queen. They are placed face down, shuffled about and you pick one. You then replace it, they are shuffled and again you pick one. Assuming the bloke is playing it fair – what are the outcomes and their chances?**

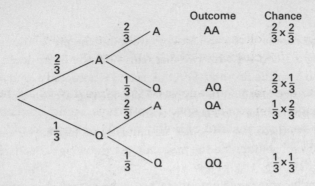

You work across the tree diagram from the left. Each set of lines from a point shows the outcomes from that event. To start with you can pick an ace (A) or a queen (Q). The chances of $\frac{2}{3}$ for the A and $\frac{1}{3}$ for the Q are written in. (Note that the chances on branches that come from the same point add up to 1.) Then the same options appear again to go with whichever card you first picked, giving a total of 4 outcomes. Because the second result was independent of the first, you can get the chance of each outcome by multiplying the fractions on the branches that link to it. E.g. the chances of picking an ace then a queen are $\frac{2}{3} \times \frac{1}{3} = \frac{2}{9}$. If you check it, you'll see that the list of the 4 chances at the end adds up to 1.

For practice, use a tree diagram to work out the chance of throwing a 5 or a 6 with a die and then an even number. (Answers on page 317.)

F: Probability spaces
We've already looked at one of these on page 294. Now let's look at a couple of possible questions.

The weather forecast for the two days you've booked at Scumpool-on-Sea says:

Day 1: 0·2 chance of rain, 0·7 chance of snow
Day 2: 0·4 chance of rain, 0·2 chance of snow

If it never rains and snows on the same day, what's the chance that you can spend both days being bombed by seagulls instead of being rained or snowed on?

I knew it!

The chance of all the possible outcomes adds up to 1, so you can work out that the chance of neither rain nor snow is 0.1 on Day 1 and 0.4 on Day 2. These events are independent so we can multiply to find the chance of no rain or snow on either day = 0.1 × 0.4 = 0.04.

If the question asked you to draw out a probability space, it should look like this. There are 100 little squares on the grid, so each square represents a chance of $\frac{1}{100}$. The four shaded squares represent the chances of both days being rainless and snowless, so that indicates a chance of 0·04 or 4%.

297

Can you work out the chance of snow on Day 1 and rain on Day 2 using both methods? What's the chance of rain on both days?

Answers on page 317.

You throw a die and then pick a card from a full shuffled pack. What chance is there that the card shows a lower number than the die? (Ace counts as 1.)

It's much harder to work out the acceptable outcomes here just by thinking about them or using a tree diagram. So this is the kind of question where it's a good idea to draw the probability space.

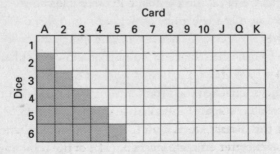

This probability space has 13 divisions along the top to represent the 13 different card values. (In a full deck the chance of each number appearing is equal.) Down the side are 6 divisions to represent the six numbers on the die. The shaded area shows the region where the card number is lower than the die. (E.g. when the card = 3 and the die = 5, the appropriate square is shaded). You'll see there are 15 shaded squares on the grid and 6 × 13 = 78 squares in total. Therefore the chance is $\frac{15}{78} = \frac{5}{26}$.

Looking at this diagram, what's the chance of throwing a 3 or higher, AND picking a card showing 9 or higher? (Answer on page 317.)

H: Sampling and probability

You know that 25 million people watched TV between 8 and 10 p.m. last night. How many were watching the Luvvie Awards?

Obviously you can't ask them all, but you can ask some of them. (This is called taking a "sample" of the "population".) Suppose you ask 10 people and 2 say they watched the awards. This suggests that across the entire population there is a $\frac{2}{10}$ chance that each person watched the awards. You could use this to work out a total viewing figure for the awards: 25,000,000 × $\frac{2}{10}$ = 5,000,000.

Hopefully you've already realized the problem here: taking a sample of just 10 people from a population of 25,000,000 is hardly likely to give a true indication. Suppose you go on to survey 10 more people and find they ALL watched the awards. This gives a probability of $\frac{10}{10}$ that each person watched the awards.

Of course, what is a much better thing to do is to add the two results together to get a survey saying that 12 out of 20 people watched the awards. The more people you survey (the larger sample), the better estimate you can make of the total number of award viewers.

You can also use probability to get an estimate of total populations. (By the way, have you noticed we're almost at the end of the book? Let's be positive about this. . .)

You've passed your maths GCSE so the Queen releases a massive number of balloons in your honour. You know that exactly 50 balloons are blue. In the clean up afterwards, 630 balloons are recovered, 8 of which are blue. How many balloons were released?

If 8 out of the 630 were blue, this suggests that the proportion of blue balloons in the population is $\frac{8}{630}$. If the total population of balloons is P and you started with 50 blue ones, then the proportion of blue balloons to the whole population is equal to $\frac{50}{P}$. You get a little equation: $\frac{8}{630} = \frac{50}{P}$ which comes to P = 50 × 630 ÷ 8 = 3937·5.

This is the *probable* number of balloons, as it relies on the 50 blue ones being equally mixed in with all the others. Obviously you can't release half a balloon, and as chance is involved it makes sense to say the number of balloons released was about 4000.

And the best of luck from us. . .

At last! Here's the end of the book and hopefully by now it's helped you clear up a load of things you weren't sure of. You might be worried that you struggled through some bits, but be reassured, it's the same for everybody who ever took maths exams and that includes all the people who have worked on producing this GCSE guide.

As the exams approach, don't forget that you've worked hard and you deserve the best possible chance of a good result. So do yourself a favour: *don't blow it*! Don't suddenly decide at the last minute that you're just going to turn up and stare out of the window. That's as daft as saving up your money for ages and then deliberately buying something you don't like.

I don't know what came over me.

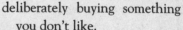

Advice for the big day

1. Remember your pen, pencil, ruler, protractor, compasses, eraser, pencil sharpener and calculator. Get them ready the night before so you don't have to hunt for them at the last minute.

2. Remember you don't have to answer the questions in the order they are written. Start with the ones which look easiest and leave the difficult ones till later.

3. Make sure you read the whole paper including the back of the last page. Sometimes there is a question lurking there that you might miss.

4. Remember you don't have to get everything right to pass so don't worry if you can't do something. Even doing part of a question can earn you valuable marks.

5. Always show your workings. They can earn you marks even if your answer is wrong.

6. If a question involves combining several sections to get a final answer, try to leave the working out until the end. Exam questions are often written with numbers that will cancel out to make the arithmetic easy.

7. Always put the units in your answer. If you don't, you may throw away marks.

8. Make it easy for the examiner to find your answer. Put it in the answer place on the paper (if there is one) or draw a line under it to make it stand out.

9. Write clearly. Don't lose marks because your 0 looks like a 6.

10. If you finish before the end, go back and check your answers. You'll be feeling calmer by then and may spot mistakes you missed earlier.

302

Even if every single question looks awful, write something down. Seeing the numbers and diagrams in your own writing may well give you the clues you need to get answers. Most important of all: when you come out of the exam it doesn't matter whether you think you've done well or done badly, what is important is that you know that you gave it your best shot.

By the way, what do you think examiners are like? Nasty people in uniforms who sneer and cackle with delight when they find you've made a mistake? Funnily enough they are not like that. Although you will probably never ever meet the people who mark your maths papers, you can be sure of a few things: they get colds in winter, they moan when they miss the bus, they have to change their underwear and at some point they had to take maths exams too. Examiners come in all shapes, sizes and situations so if it helps, imagine your paper is being marked by somebody's mum sitting at the kitchen table drinking cocoa with a baby dozing on her lap. It's hard to believe, but examiners know exactly what you're going through, and *they want you to do well*. It's up to you to help them by showing what you know as clearly as you can.

Remember, everybody hopes your efforts pay off with a good result, and that especially includes the team from Scholastic who put this book together to help you as best we can.

Good luck from. . .

Kjartan Poskitt (bloke who wrote it), Tracey Turner (who told him to write it), Mike Moon (who told him what to write about), Dave Watkins (who told him what to cross out), Marina Chester (who kept them all on speaking terms), Pythagoras (Greek bloke who invented a lot of it in the first place), Diana Kimpton (who checked the sums), Polly Dunbar (who filled in the gaps with pictures), Raymond Turvey (who sorted out the graphs), Michelle Hearne (who put everything in place).

303

Answers

Numbers
Page 18
1. Four hundred and thirty-five; seventy-two thousand and five; thirty-four million, two hundred and seventy-eight thousand, two hundred and one.

2. a) 121 122 211 212 **b)** 4576 4756 5467 5674

Page 19
6057; 1709; 13,905; 85

Page 20
129,033 rivets and 38 apples. If you got 177 rivets or you got 31,958 apples then you MUST be more careful! You have to work out when to multiply or when to divide. For the first sum you should have worked out 4779 × 27 and for the second 1102 ÷ 29.

Page 25
a) 5081·3 **b)** 11900 **c)** 0·0000427 (Well done if you got this one right! The sum should be 0·050813 ÷ 1190 = 50813 ÷ 1,000,000 ÷ 119 ÷ 10 = 50813 ÷ 119 ÷ 10,000,000 = 427 ÷ 10,000,000 = 0·0000427)

Page 28
a) 25 **b)** $\frac{1}{32}$ **c)** $3^{-5} = \frac{1}{3^5} = \frac{1}{243}$ **d)** $4^{-\frac{1}{2}} = \frac{1}{4^{\frac{1}{2}}} = \frac{1}{2}$ **e)** $\left(\frac{9}{25}\right)^{-\frac{1}{2}} = \left(\frac{25}{9}\right)^{\frac{1}{2}}$
$= \frac{5}{3} = 1\frac{2}{3}$ **f)** $(64 \times 27)^{\frac{1}{3}} = 64^{\frac{1}{3}} \times 27^{\frac{1}{3}} = 4 \times 3 = 12$

Page 29
15. It's the 4th triangle number + 5. Incidentally, the 5th triangle is how the 15 red balls are set out at the start of a game of snooker.

Page 29
$7 \times 8 \div 2 = 28$; $20 \times 21 \div 2 = 210$; $99 \times 100 \div 2 = 4950$

Page 30
1, 2, 4, 8, 16, 32; 1, 2, 5, 10, 25, 50; 1, 2, 3, 4, 6, 8, 9, 12, 18, 24, 36, 72

Page 31
<u>31</u> 33 35 <u>37</u> 39 <u>41</u> <u>43</u> 45 <u>47</u> 49 51 <u>53</u> 55 57 <u>59</u>

Page 35
1. a) 2, 7, 7, 11 **b)** 3, 7, 7, 7 **c)** 5, 7, 19
2. $x = 3$ $y = 2$

Page 38
1. $\frac{3}{4}$ $\frac{6}{13}$ $\frac{3}{11}$ **2.** $2\frac{3}{4}$ $4\frac{3}{10}$ $4\frac{3}{7}$ **3.** $\frac{13}{5}$ $\frac{31}{17}$ $\frac{76}{7}$

Page 39
a) $\frac{1}{2}$ **b)** $3\frac{1}{3}$ **c)** $3\frac{1}{2}$ **d)** $1\frac{1}{4}$

Page 40
a) $\frac{1}{3}$ **b)** $\frac{5}{8}$ **c)** $\frac{9}{16}$ **d)** $\frac{11}{20}$ **e)** $1\frac{9}{20}$

305

Page 41
a) 2   **b)** £8.40   **c)** 665   **d)** £4.25

Page 42
a) 39%   **b)** 2160%   **c)** 2·674%

Page 43
1. 25%   **2.** 170%

Page 43
a) 13·12%, $\frac{3}{8}$, 61%, 0·72, $\frac{4}{5}$, $\frac{7}{8}$, 2·5   **b)** $\frac{3}{10}$, $\frac{30}{99}$, 33%, $\frac{1}{3}$

Page 45
80 cars in total, 44 cars left

Page 52
1. a) $\frac{30-20}{2+8} = \frac{10}{10} = 1$ **b)** $300 \times 40 = 12,000$
2. a) 120,000,000   **b)** 0.042   **c)** 4   **d)** 6000

Page 54
$-2°$

Page 59
1. £12: £24: £36   **2.** 63 animals, 35 sheep, 7 pigs

Page 62
$y = 15 \times \frac{170}{240} = 10·625$ litres

Page 63
C has gone up from 5 to 7 so it has been multiplied by $\frac{7}{5}$.
Therefore D must be divided by $\frac{7}{5}$ which is the same as $\times \frac{5}{7}$. So
"d" $= 3 \times \frac{5}{7} = 2\frac{1}{7}$.

Page 63
$t = 35 \times \frac{10}{12} = 29{\cdot}167$ minutes; $s = 10 \times \frac{35}{20} = 17{\cdot}5$ km/h

Page 65
400 Newtons

Page 68
Maximum volume is $12{\cdot}5 \times 25{\cdot}5 \times 2{\cdot}25 = 717$ m^3
Minimum volume is $11{\cdot}5 \times 24{\cdot}5 \times 2{\cdot}15 = 606$ m^3

Page 70
$1{\cdot}2$, $3{\cdot}14$, $\sqrt{\frac{4}{9}}$, $(4{\cdot}2)^3$

Page 71
a) $2\sqrt{5}$ **b)** $6\sqrt{2}$ **c)** $4\sqrt{6}$

Page 76
$5{\cdot}61 \times 10^6$, $3{\cdot}24 \times 10^{-7}$, $7{\cdot}298 \times 10^{-8}$

Page 78
$7{\cdot}08 \times 10^{17}$

Algebra
Page 89
a) $12p^2 + 8p$ **b)** $2y^2 + 7y - 4$ **c)** $2 - q - 3q^2$ **d)** $3r + s - 6rs - 2s^2$

Page 90
a) $a(3 + b)$ **b)** $2q(2p + q)$ **c)** $2c(1 - 2c)$ **d)** $3a - b^2 \ldots$ there's nothing that will factorize here!

Page 92
$(x + 6)(x - 3)$

Page 92
a) $(x + 10)(x + 2)$ **b)** $(d + 3)(d - 10)$ **c)** $(a + 5)(a - 2)$
d) $(4 - p)(2 + p)$

Page 97
$(3 + x)(5 - 4x)$

Page 102
a) $x = 6$ **b)** $y = 5$ **c)** $y = 1$ **d)** $x = -2$

Page 102
The number is 7.

Page 103
Spud got £2.20, Dreggs got £1.10 and Ringo got £1.30.

Page 103
If Paul has £x, John has £$(x + 20)$ and Petunia has £$(x + 50)$. The
equation is $x + (x + 20) + (x + 50) = 370$. When you solve it you
find Paul has £100, John has £120 and Petunia has £150.

Page 104
If e = explorers, $\frac{1}{2}(\frac{3e}{4} - 4) - 1 = 6$; $e = 24$. So 24 people
started out.

Page 106
$y = \frac{Q}{3 + a^2}$

Page 107
a) $(x-2)(x-1) = 0$ so $x = 2$ or 1 **b)** $(x-5)(x+1) = 0$ so $x = 5$ or -1
c) $(x-7)(x+2) = 0$ so $x = 7$ or -2 **d)** $(4x-1)(x+3) = 0$ so
$x = \frac{1}{4}$ or -3 **e)** $(2x+7)(2x-3) = 0$ so $x = -3\frac{1}{2}$ or $x = 1\frac{1}{2}$

Page 110
$x = \frac{2}{3}$ or $2\frac{1}{2}$. From the equation $(2x-3)(3x-5) = 5$ expand and
rearrange to make $6x^2 - 19x + 10 = 0$, then put the numbers in
the formula.

Page 120
a) elephant breathing **b)** ball **c)** bus **d)** basin of water

Page 131
The flowers cost £3.50 and the chocolates cost £2.40. (You
should have got 350 and 240 from your graph – remember you
were working in pennies.)

Page 146
Area = -8.875 (Strictly speaking this area is "negative" because
it's under the x axis.)

Page 147
Stopping distance = 8·4 miles. This answer is slightly high
because the curve of the graph dips slightly below each line on
the tops of the trapezium.

Page 147
It's not easy to read gradients very accurately, but roughly your
answers should be: after 0·2 hours acceleration = -26 mph/h and
after 0·8 hours acceleration = -14 mph/h. Notice that the
gradients are negative, which indicates the ship is slowing down.

Page 150
55 and 89

Page 154
After 6 weeks £508,000 and after 20 weeks £410,000.
Formula = £$(550,000 - 7,000n)$, but if you really wanted to impress people, you could factorize it to £$1000(550 - 7n)$.

Page 156
a) $3n - 1$ **b)** 3×2^n

Shape
Page 166
11-sided polygon: int = $147°$ and ext = $33°$
20-sided polygon: int = $162°$ and ext = $18°$

Page 176
Scalene: no symmetry. Isosceles: 1 line of reflective symmetry, no rotational symmetry. Equilateral: 3 lines of reflective and 3 positions of rotational symmetry.

Page 179
Triangles K and L are congruent. Notice that the $80°$ angle in L is the unmarked angle in J and K. (Remember all three angles must add to $180°$.)

Page 180
ABCD does not tell us how long sides AB, BC and DC are, even though we know all the angles. (Angle C = $360 - 90 - 80 - 70 = 120°$.) PQRS has the $90°$ between $120°$ and $80°$. All the others

310

have the 90° between 70° and 120°. JKLM has the 5 cm side between 120° and 90°. So EFGH and TUVW are congruent.

Page 182
VU = 1·17 cm; JK = 3·6 cm; PQ = 5·4 cm.

Page 182
CA = 25. DA = 12 because the ratio of DA to BD is the same as the ratio of EA to CE, which is 15:10 or 3:2.

Page 185
5,12,13 is right-angled. 7,8,17 cannot exist.

Page 186
The line is $\sqrt{6^2 + 3^2} = \sqrt{49} = 6·71$.

Page 191
DC = 5·389 m

Page 191
CE = 1·961 m

Page 194
y = 37·87°; p = 27·49°; q = 62·51°

Page 195
y = 9·24 cm

Page 196
The angles must add up to 180, so ψ = 180 − 55 − 40·29 = 84·71°. Go on to use the formula to find that s = 4·62 m.

Page 198
$\theta = 73 \cdot 40°$; t = 2·90 cm

Page 203
20·94 km and 300·5°

Page 205
Use the sine rule to get AD = $14 \times \frac{\sin 65°}{\sin 75°}$ = 13·14 km and BD = $14 \times \frac{\sin 40°}{\sin 75°}$ ≈ 9·32 km. Written out properly: The dinghy was 13·14 km from lifeboat A and 9·32 km from lifeboat B.

Page 211

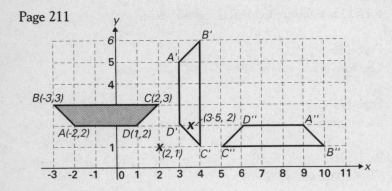

Page 213
(4·5,0·5) – 90°

Page 216
$(-1, -0·5) - \frac{1}{3}$

Page 217
$\mathbf{b} = \left(\begin{smallmatrix} 2 \\ -2 \end{smallmatrix}\right)$; $\mathbf{c} = \left(\begin{smallmatrix} -2 \\ -2 \end{smallmatrix}\right)$; $\mathbf{d} = \left(\begin{smallmatrix} -4 \\ 0 \end{smallmatrix}\right)$; inverse of $\mathbf{d} = \left(\begin{smallmatrix} 4 \\ 0 \end{smallmatrix}\right)$.

Page 219
a) $\begin{pmatrix} -7 \\ 4 \end{pmatrix}$ **b)** $\begin{pmatrix} 11 \\ 6 \end{pmatrix}$ **c)** $\begin{pmatrix} 0 \\ 0 \end{pmatrix} = 0$

Page 220
It was rotated 90° anticlockwise around point A to produce image A. It was converted with a scale factor of $-\frac{1}{2}$ through point B to produce image B. It was reflected in the dotted line to produce the image C. It was translated using the column vector $\begin{pmatrix} 6 \\ -1 \end{pmatrix}$ to produce image D.

Page 222
ABCD has been translated using the vector $\begin{pmatrix} 5 \\ 0 \end{pmatrix}$.

Page 223
Centre = (1,1); angle = – 90° or 90° clockwise.

Page 225
1. 12 inches = 1 foot ≈ 30 cm, therefore 1 inch ≈ $\frac{30}{12}$ ≈ 2·5 cm. So 3 inches ≈ 7·5 cm.
2. 27 km = 16·875 miles ≈ 16 miles and (0·875 × 1760) yards = 16 miles and 1540 yards.
3. 11 gallons = 88 pints ≈ 50·16 litres costing £67·72.

Page 231
1. Circle E: area = 452·39 cm^2; perimeter = 75·40 cm.
2. Circle F: diameter = 12·36 mm. (If area = πr^2 then $r = \sqrt{\frac{120}{\pi}}$ = 6·18. Don't forget the question asked for the DIAMETER which is 2 × r.)
3. Circle G: area = 50929·58 m^2. (First work out the radius which is $\frac{800}{2\pi}$ = 127·32 m. Then the area.)

Page 233
Cylinder surface area = $2\pi r^2 + 2\pi rh = 2\pi r(r + h)$
Triangular prism surface area = $2 \times \frac{1}{2}ab + (a + b + c)h = ab + (a + b + c)h$

Page 241

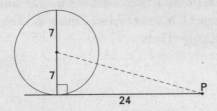

If the diameter is 14 cm, the radius is 7 cm. This gives you a right-angled triangle with shorter sides 7 cm and 24 cm. The length from the point to the centre is the hypotenuse of this triangle, so $(\text{length})^2 = 7^2 + 24^2$. When you solve this you get: distance of P to the centre = 25 cm.

Page 245
Imagine AC is the chord. The angle in the segment is $A\hat{B}C$ and the opposite angle is $U\hat{A}C$. You've got to watch out for this sort of thing!

Page 246
$o = 180° - m = 180° - 130° = 50°$. Angle p is in the opposite segment to angle l, so $p = 65°$; $q = p = 65°$; $r = 180° - (l + n + q) = 180° - (65° + 25° + 65°) = 25°$.

Page 247
$A\hat{B}O = 36.9°$; $B\hat{O}A = 53.1°$; $O\hat{B}D = 17.5°$; $B\hat{O}D = 72.5°$

Page 251

$\overrightarrow{RP}$ $\overrightarrow{PO}$ OR $\overrightarrow{RQ}$ $\overrightarrow{QO}$

Page 256

BAC = 70° (y = 20° and x = 50°). Use the cosine rule to get **a**: a^2 = $(200)^2$ + $(60)^2$ − 2 × 200 × 60 × cos 70 which works out as **a** = 188·13 km/h. Use the sine rule to get angle AĈB: sin AĈB = 60 × $\frac{\sin 70}{188.13}$ comes out as AĈB = 17·44°. Check the diagram to see that the bearing of **a** is (130 − 17·44)° = 112·56°. So the pilot needs to set the helicopter at 188·13 km/h on a bearing of 112·56°.

Data

Page 259

1. It depends what you're doing with the tins! If the tins are just for you at home, then about 8–10 will give you a good idea. Any less and you can't be sure, any more and you're starting to open tins pointlessly. However, if you're putting the tins out on supermarket shelves, you need to be extremely confident of what they are! Open at least 50.

2. Test them all! Even just one leak could be critical.

3. Two or three, and pick matches from different parts of the box.

Page 276

The mode is 637 g because it occurs twice (the other weights only occur once). The median is halfway between 665 g and 670 g = 667·5 g. The mean is 15,853 ÷ 24 = 660·54 g.

Page 277

The mean mileage is 35,681.

Page 278

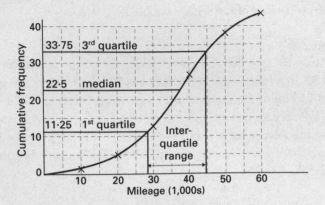

Interquartile range = 46,000 – 29,000 = 17,000 miles
Median value = 37,000 miles

Page 281
The mode group is 60–70 mph (the biggest area). Half the cars did not go over 60 mph, because about half the area of all columns was to the left of the 60 mph line.

Page 288
Mean weight of bags of chips = 660·54 g and s.d. = 53·77.

Page 290
Dice: $\frac{3}{6}$ or $\frac{1}{2}$ or 50%. Sweets: $\frac{8}{10}$ or $\frac{4}{5}$ or 80%.

Page 293
White or yellow = $\frac{5}{15} + \frac{3}{15} = \frac{8}{15}$. Not purple or orange: the chances of purple are $\frac{1}{15}$, the chances of orange are $\frac{2}{15}$. Add these to find the chances of purple or orange are $\frac{3}{15}$. Therefore the chances of NOT having purple or orange are $(1 - \frac{3}{15}) = \frac{12}{15} = \frac{4}{5}$.

Page 295
The probability of throwing a double is $\frac{6}{36} = \frac{1}{6}$.

Page 296

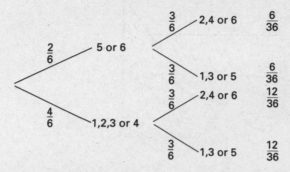

The chance of throwing a 5 or a 6 with a die and then an even number are $\frac{6}{36} = \frac{1}{6}$.

Page 298
0·28 and 0·08

Page 299
$\frac{20}{78} = \frac{10}{39}$